ON TIME AND IN STEP: REUNION ON THE GLORY ROAD

By Gloria I. Joseph, Ph.D.

On Time and In Step:
Reunion on The Glory Road

Library of Congress Control Number: 2009920052

ISBN 978-0-578-00249-1

Manufactured & Published in the United States Virgin Islands by
Winds of Change Press
Christiansted, St. Croix Virgin Islands 00820
windsofchangepress@gmail.com

Front & Back Cover Designs By: Dr. ChenziRa D. Kahina
Front Cover Illustration Designed By: Dara M. Cooper
Front Cover Photos in Oval from left to right- Mother Jones, Geronimo, Amelia Earhart and Babe Ruth
Back Cover Photographs of Gloria I. Joseph, Ph.D.:
       Upper Left taken in Amherst, Massachusetts in 1986 By Jill Lewis
       Lower Left taken in Christiansted, St. Croix VI in 2008 By Dr. ChenziRa D. Kahina

Dedication

This book is dedicated to persons living and persons departed who have made indelible and positive contributions to my personal and professional life.

It is with deep love and gratitude that I dedicate this book to **Ethlyn Marie Joseph**, my oldest sister who was a great storyteller. The oldest of eight siblings, at bedtime she often told us incredibly imaginative stories. She could have been a very fine author.

It is with the deepest appreciation that I dedicate this book to **Toni Cade Bambara**. Many, years ago, when this book was in its embryonic stage I sent a draft to Toni. She responded with a five-page critique and much encouragement. I sent her a second draft and again she responded with a three-page critique, advice, and enthusiastic encouragement. As I wrote, I frequently referred to her detailed advisement. Thank you Toni and thanks for the Nat Turner T-shirt. You said that I was the only one you knew who would wear it.

Over decades of teaching, many outstanding students contributed to my development as a professor and mentor. They thanked me in both written and spoken words for my role as their mentor and in their social, political, and academic development. In return, I was gratified as they practiced and displayed important aspects of my teaching efforts in their chosen professions.

I therefore dedicate this book to the following former students:

Dr. Irving Presley McPhail, Chief Operating Officer for National Action Council for Minority Engineers: Former Chancellor of State College, Baltimore County, Maryland.
Dr. Ernest D. Green, Professor of Sociology, Brooklyn College, New York
Ann Hackler, Co-Director of the Institute for Musical Arts, Goshen, Massachusetts
Dean Willesse Commisiong, Director of Balfour Center for Multicultural Affairs, Providence College, Rhode Island

Dr. Zala Highsmith Taylor, Retired Professor Medgar Evers College, Brooklyn, New York

Dr. Robert (Bob) Moore, (deceased) Former Resource Director for Council for Interracial Books for Children: An exceptionally gifted writer, outstanding student and one of the most sincerely devoted anti-racist practitioner I have ever met.

Acknowledgements

There are many persons to whom I am indebted for the publication of this book, and they are NOT too numerous to mention. I thank the following for their varied, valuable and substantial contributions.

- Dr. ChenziRa Davis Kahina who was a steady and resolute source of mental and spiritual inspiration. She was humorous when we reached an impasse in deliberations and very respectful of my idiosyncrasies. Moreover, she was my "computer expert" retrieving, editing, realigning and laying out materials I lost, repairing recalcitrant computers and technologically speaking, she made the publication possible.
- Lynda Muhammad posed critical questions and offered suggestions as she assisted in the typing of the manuscript. She helped to bring a sparkle and verve to the chapters with her shrewd understanding of human nature.
- Sheelagh Fromer, my fellow book club member and her son Michael Fromer were extremely helpful in providing relevant information concerning Native Americans in Chapter 2.
- Howard Francis, a long time friend, who at Christmas, Kwanzaa and birthdays gave me wonderful books by and about Africans and African-Americans. These books were pillars of foundation for my research.
- Chrystos, my Native American soul sister, artist and poet of exceptional talent, graciously granted me permission to use her poetry. Megwetch (*a Native American term for "thank you"*), Chrystos.
- Olassee Davis, a Native Virgin Islander, is an ecologist who lives on St. Croix. I thank him for his article, "*The Awe and Fascination of Cloud*s." It provided information endemic to the novel's setting.
- Zala Highsmith Taylor, my colleague and dear friend, and her husband, Fitzgerald Taylor, my "partner in laughter", compose my private cheering squad. They "loved" whatever I wrote, extended compliments and encouraged me to "write on."

- Sonia Sanchez was a solid source of reliability. Whenever I called she graciously offered support, assistance and willingly gave valuable advice.
- Attorney Lisa Carter Moorhead's sophistication, wit and flexibility were deeply appreciated as she interacted with personnel involved in the formal and legal aspects of publishing.
- Sayeeda Carter, a public school teacher, was instrumental in providing a perspective on today's generation. She gave first-hand information on the language, interests, the familiar and lack of familiar knowledge students' hold concerning re-known historical figures.
- Eneid Routte Gomez, a stellar writer whose copyediting complimented my creativity in a distinct Afro-centric manner.
- And most importantly, I acknowledge Helga Emde, who supported and sustained me while living through the "partner pangs" of life with a writer who anguishes over deadlines but "can't miss that golf game."

About the Author

In this section I would like to inform the reader about facts, events and activities that hold particularly significant joyful and memorable life time experiences. My parents, Ida Helene David Joseph and Daniel Oswald Joseph, were born in St. Croix, Virgin Islands and I am number seven of eight children. I am the grand niece of Casper Holstein, the great Crucian philanthropist and Harlem numbers king. I graduated from New York University, New York, B.S; The City College of New York, M.S.; Cornell University, Ithaca, New York, Ph.D. In between academia, here is what was truly a meaningful education. The following are not in any chronological order.

Raised honeybees and had an apiary of over 100 hives in St. Croix. As a participant in the Citizen Ambassador Program, in 1991 along with bee collective member Sadiq Abdullah, attended an International Symposium on bees in China, the world's largest producer of honey. The three week tour of apiaries, factories and country side bee hives, in Beijing, Shanghai, Nanjing and Hangzhou besides Hong Kong, concluded with an Authentic Cuisine Menu of 23 courses, starting with Green Tea, ending with fresh fruit, (*grapes*) and in between, Turtle Soup, (*with feet and claws*) and Quail Eggs w/mung beans (*100-year old eggs put in ground to rot*). Rode in a rickshaw and climbed the Great Wall of China. (*Not to the top.*)

In France visited the Lascaux Caves (*with prehistoric painting*) just before the caves were closed to the public. During same trip visited the resort of Josephine Baker with her multicultural children and I danced with Baker at her resort nightclub.

Translated for Mahalia Jackson in Paris, France where she was performing. When the audience requested her to sing "In ze ooper room" and Mahalia kept asking, "what?" I shouted out, "In the Upper Room" and Mahalia said, "ooohhh"; Rode an elephant in India and saw the Glowing splendor of the Taj Mahal at night; and Rode a camel in Cairo, Egypt to "study" the colossal pyramids and mysterious Sphinx situated on top of the Giza plateau.

In Botswana, Southern Africa, working on a Reading Project I discovered that Bessie Head, the brilliant South African writer, lived next door. Established a relationship and visited her on a daily basis. After departing Botswana we maintained a writing correspondence that continued until her death in 1986; and Scattered the ashes of Audre Lorde, a self defined, 'mother, poet, lesbian, feminist, activist,' at Pele's Crater and the Women's Sacred Place in Hawaii; Kumme Lanke Lake in Berlin, Germany; the Caribbean waters surrounding Buck Island in St. Croix.

During the 1960 Olympics in Rome, Italy, stayed at The Vatican because the rooms reserved for DAC (*Department of Army Civilians*) were not completed; To gain admission to the Vatican we had to give the 'password' to the Swiss Guards; It looked very dramatic but all we were saying was the name of our Spartan sleeping quarters, "Santa Maria"; Was invited by Nawal el Sadawi to attend The Seventh International Conference of the Arab Women's Solidarity Association in Cairo, May 2005; and Delivered my essay, "*My Journey's Through Feminism: National; Caribbean; International*", that Meridian magazine rejected and women worldwide were extremely appreciative of.

Visited Cuba three times: One time with a delegation of Black women Writers- Toni Cade Bambara, Audre Lorde, Mari Evans, Rosa Guy, Jane Cortez, Louise Merriweather and Vertamae Grosvenor and met Pablo Neruda; A second time I was "chaperone" for a group of New York City, 'Sullivanians', (*Harry Stack Sullivan devotees*); and A third time with a group of educators from various stateside universities.

As the founder of SISA (*Sisterhood in Support of Sisters in South Africa*) in 1984, the organization raised funds that were sent directly to two women's self-help groups Zamani Soweto Sisters and the Maggie Magaba Trust; During a trip to South Africa to meet the women and observe their productivities, I was accompanied by Ada Griffin, a professional film maker, and we made a compelling video. Highlights of the trip were the camaraderie and individual interviews and excursions through the Shantytowns with Ellen Kuzwayo and Winnie Mandela.

At Cornell University during the *"Cornell With Guns"* episode in April 1969, and I was the only faculty member in the *"Take-Over"* building with the students. We exited from the building, females on the inside with the protection of the Black male students with guns and a supporting line of SDS (*Students for a Democratic Society*) members on either side. Outside of that protection was an angry mob and policemen and the National Guard was on alert. The Associated Press photographer who captured the rifles, bandoliers and the exit won the Pulitzer Prize for the best photograph of 1969.

Spent three years in Europe, two years stationed in Mannheim, Germany, one year in Paris, France as a school psychologist and reading specialist with the DAC (*Department of Army Civilians*). During that time one of my outlandish adventures was as a novice skiing down the Matterhorn, in Switzerland. One of my more sobering adventures was seeing *The Passion Play* in Oberamagau, Austria while staying in the village with the 'actors and actresses'.

Traveled across the United States in the '70's, from New York to California, with three friends, Chuck, Floyd and Diane, in my red Buick that we called, *"The Red Badge of Courage."* Chuck, born Charles Trimble on Pine Ridge Reservation in South Dakota; Floyd "Red Crow" Westerman, also a Sioux from Pine Ridge Reservation. Later, as an actor, Floyd was the Medicine Man in *"Dances With Wolves"*; and Diane Wallach, a Jewish young woman from Augusta, Missouri. This integrated group visited Native American reservations, attended a powwow, explored the Grand Canyon and all during the tour neatly dealt with all types of racism in hotels, casinos, restaurants and on the road.

`

Table of Contents

Note: After each chapter are "Glossary & Endnotes"

Introduction and Overview

"gonna meet my ol' friend on that Old Glory Road"....spiritual

On Time and In Step: Reunion on The Glory Road is a novel based on actual historical figures that have departed from the earth, but live again in the hereafter. Often the elderly will talk about their visions of meeting friends on that *magnificent Glory Road*. The hereafter, that *magnificent Glory Road*, becomes the stage for heroic figures from the past, to meet and reunite, discuss and analyze the past, predict and expostulate about the future and rejoice and celebrate the peace and beauty of their final home.

The contents of the novel are based on the interplay of the lives of the characters as they were in their own times, juxtaposed with current issues and popular personalities in the present world. The setting for the novel is the firmament, or heavens, the dwelling place of the spirits and righteous people after death. It is laid out in communities with major roads, avenues, lanes, parks, gardens and lovely comfortable homes for all the inhabitants. No Homeless People Here!

The major thoroughfare in the heavens is the Glory Road. It is wide, curved and air paved. Rows of sculptured-like clouds embrace the road as magnificent sunrays encourage a hydroponics floral extravaganza along the roadside.

The section of heaven where Malcolm and Sojourner dwell is called Revolutionary's Retreat and is the resting grounds for those persons in history, -women and men of all races, cultures and beliefs, - who in their lives took radical actions to help create a just world. They are called, "late revolutionaries." Radical actions refers to actions taken that are a marked departure from traditional legislative politics, along with a belief that reform measures are not the most effective or productive way of dealing with the severity of problems resulting from systematic racist, sexist, heterosexist, religious and economic oppressions.

Malcolm X meets Sojourner Truth on an early morning stroll on the Glory Road. They continue their walk throughout the book. Along the way, they meet other residents and the discussions and interactions compose the contents of the novel. There is a gregarious mixture of individuals: W.E.B. Dubois, Fanny Lou Hamer, Nanny the Maroon, Chief Sitting Bull, Paul Robeson, Moms Mabley, Bessie Smith, and Frederick Douglas, among others. There are many persons, entertainers, scholars, athletes and others, who live in the various communities but do not qualify for residency in Revolutionary's Retreat. However, the uniqueness of their personalities and their laudable contributions to society makes their inclusion worthwhile.

The ages of the characters are determined by their age at their death plus the number of years to the present. However, the rarefied air and healthy living arrests the aging process. The individuals arrive in the clothes of their times and many continue to wear the same styles, while others adorn themselves in modern fashion. The rarefied air regulates body temperatures so no matter what clothing they wear, individuals remain comfortable.

Each residential community is equipped with several "Time Gazers." This magnificent celestial technological apparatus allows the residents to beam in on all parts of the world and view the events on a large screen. In this way, they can get a good look-see at what is happening below and compare their pasts to the present. Intercommunity travel takes place on the cloud rails or strata-plane. Intracommunity travel is by foot. The inhabitants enjoy the beauty of their multifaceted cloudlands, high above the pollution and nuclear fallout, and they rejoice with the absence of violence and with the presence of serenity.

Various characters discuss current and classic subjects and topics in their voices. The progressive, wise, and astute political visions, the wit, style and, humor of Malcolm and Sojourner are captured in their commentaries. Given new life are the voices of two of America's revered and honored personalities.

Sojourner Truth was a deeply religious woman who believed that her purpose was to follow God's words, to bring His message to the people. She believed she was His messenger. She possessed great intellect and uncanny wit, coupled with a keen ability to see through the pretense and get to the core of personal and societal problems. Sojourner had a calm air about her and a fearless approach to problem solving. These characteristics made her one of the most popular and respected figures in Revolutionary's Retreat.

Similarly, Malcolm's popularity was based on his faith, charisma and a firm belief in the power of the people. He was a different kind of messenger. Educating, organizing, and empowering oppressed people actualized his quest for liberation/freedom for his people.

Sojourner spoke directly to the oppressors while Malcolm worked directly with the oppressed and declared the oppressors as the enemy of the people. Sojourner felt that her message was to work with all of God's people including the "enemies" whom she saw as ultra oppressed people and deeply in need of salvation.

Their ideologies may appear opposed but they are just different expressions of the same reality. This African epistemological principle expresses a complementary of differences as opposed to a strict, rigid polarity of differences.

In Nell Irvin Painter's outstanding biography of Sojourner Truth entitled Sojourner Truth: A Life, A Symbol, she states that, "Sojourner Truth has become American material culture's female equivalent of Malcolm X. Her image demonstrates the wearer or owner's political correctness." (*NIP:pg 275*)

Malcolm and Sojourner's unwavering adherence to the ethics of personal accountability contribute heavily to their revered positions in the Retreat. They are the chosen two protagonists for this novel.

Sojourner's speech remains unclarified. It is recorded that for the first nine or ten years of her life her language was low Dutch. Her way of speaking experienced gradual changes in speech patterns, dialects and pronunciation. The Dutch language influenced her pronunciation; she learned English that was at times grammatically correct; her colloquial style developed later in her life and she picked up some Black stylistic speech along the way.

In the novel, Sojourner's speech is Basic English grammar with a colloquial touch. The only remnants of Dutch influence are an occasional substitution of "d" for "th" in words like those, there, this and that. The word children will be "chilluns" and women, "wimmin." This is done to make Sojourner's speech more readable and understandable.

Gloria I. Joseph, Ph.D., November 2008

Chapter One
Conversation While Strolling Along The Glory Road Boulevard

The road was paved with air. The color of the air combined sand from the painted-desert and windblown tufts of angel's hair. The road curved and meandered with a peaceful mind of its own, in harmony with drifting banks of delicate rose, lavender and peach colored cumulus clouds. A tall, stately, lean, figure moved easily on the road in her oft repaired brown, walking boots and a lightweight gray, woolen shawl protecting her shoulders from too much early morning dew. A shoe top length full moss green skirt and the African walking stick she carried moved in rhythm with her leisurely yet energetic gait. The ebony walking stick was a much-treasured gift from Patrice Lumumba. In place of her usual well-worn white bonnet, she sported a new one with black, yellow, and red trim.

As she rounded a corner, she recognized her charismatic and close friend with his well-proportioned, angular frame and close-cropped reddish hair. He was inspecting the fading remains of a night blooming cereus - one of the most beautiful flowers on the boulevard with multiple delicate shades of greens, yellows and whites, - but as the name implies it opens at night and lasts through early morning.

"Good mornin' brudder, I see you're admiring the early blooms. Early bird catches the bloom", she punned.

Clad in a wrinkle proof white shirt, tan slacks, and cordovan shoes, he was filled with the vigor of the sunrise atmosphere on the Glory Road here in Revolutionary's Retreat. His smile was cheery and bright as he returned the greeting, "As-Salaam Alaikum, sister. With that new bonnet I may have to address you as Madame Fashion."

"Brudder Malcolm, you may have discarded your slave name and put a number or letter in its place, but I have a God-given name, -

Sojourner Truth", she replied folding her arms across her breasts and drawing herself up a few inches taller than her five feet eleven inches. Now a days young folks, particularly dose in the music world, call demselves names like 50 cents and Trick Daddy, Soljah Boy and Snoop Dogg. Past generations had regular, tolerable names. Now the one called Chamillionaire, making millions and shouting out cuss words, calling' wimmin derogatory names, - shameful, that's what it is, shameful."

Malcolm bowed slightly from the waist, smiled earnestly, saying, "Good morning sister Sojourner, and my apologies ma'am. And what stratochannel have you been watching that featured rap artists and the hip-hop generation?"

"Beamed in on one of those shows featurin' rapsters or whatever you call 'em. They dancing singing' and performing' in silly sitcoms all to the tune of money. And they sure do make millions and billions, buying sports cars, extra sport cars, limousines, private planes and gold everything. Black folks have come a long way from chains on the coffle, to chain gangs, to gold chains 'round dere necks."

Knowing that Sojourner did not appreciate being held up too long from her morning stroll, Malcolm politely inquired, "Mind if I join you on your morning sojourn?"

"Be much obliged", responded Sojourner. "And how is Mrs. Betty Shabazz doin' these days?"

"Very well, thank you. She was getting ready to visit sisters Ella Baker, Fundi, as we call her, and Rosa Parks."

As they walked, they passed Croton Lane with the multicolored leaves forming a backdrop for the duo. Malcolm resumed the conversation. "Sister Sojourner, it was back in 1940 that our brother, W.E.B. DuBois, said that most whites want Negroes to amuse them. Looking at some of the popular Black hip-hop artists, athletes, and entertainers you can see the truth in that statement.

8

Sometimes it looks like they're going back to the minstrel show days, you know, when wearing black face and acting ignorant and foolish was the trademark of Black entertainment for whites."

"Most of the time I'd rather NOT look." Sojourner interjected quickly with a, "Humpf, such wickedness, and nakedness aren't fit for the eyes of adults much less chilluns. Those videos, if all that ruckus wasn't going on in the background, most folks wouldn't even be looking'. Too much money made from wickedness and spent on sinfulness."

Malcolm pushed his glasses further back on the bridge of his nose as he concentrated on what Sojourner was saying. "Sister, the truth of the matter is that most Black entertainers today are controlled by white agents, bosses, and companies. Those record companies producing those self-deprecating, demeaning, sexist, rap artist's records and CDs will continue to produce that trash as long as people buy them."

"Now those young wimmin, I wonder if they know how they are being insulted, degraded or as they say now a days, victimized, in those lyrics? And just look at some of those young at'letes, getting' in to all sorts of trouble wid the law. They need to follow in the footsteps of people like Arthur Ashe, Jackie Robinson, and Paul Robeson. In that way they can learn some dignifinery and sensibility."

Sojourner had a way of inventing words to suit her needs. Malcolm filed 'dignifinery' in his mind and said, "So you've been watching rap artists and now athletes. I didn't know you were into sports too."

"It's only when I visit folks in At'letes Arena do I see the sporting' events. But sometimes I don't know what sport I'm watching. At those big football games after a touchdown, son, I nevah seen such carryin' on by them players! All sorts of shakin' and high steppin' like they doing' the cake- walk and jerkin' their bodies like they spastic. Such a carryin' on, struttin' like peacocks and head pecking'. Now some of them get down on one knee, bless their selves, and say a little prayer. That's what I like."

Malcolm smiled broadly and said, "What's that you say, Sojourner? How they act?"

"You know what I'm talkin' about. You used to do that stuff when you were doing your high flying dance steps on the dance floor at the Roseland Ballroom."

Malcolm could not resist chiding Sojourner a bit. "Oh you mean when the players do that little celebration dance, sort of like this" and he started mimicking the ballplayers, doing some variations of the electric slide and the old boogie-woogie.

Sojourner cocked her head to one side, thumped her stick on the air-paved road and gazed with amusement as she said, "Son, it's too early in the mornin' for you to be carryin' on wit' that foolishness."

Malcolm ended his performance and, still amused, said seriously, "They do get carried away with the thrill and excitement of it all. But the football players aren't the only ones doing what we old folks up here see as silly antics. When those basketball players do that dunk and swing on the rims with their legs bent, they could be orangutans swinging from limb to limb. And they get millions for entertaining the public with their athletic abilities."

Sojourner paused, shook her head as she emphasized her words, "Money, money, it's all 'bout money. They put money before God, decency and family."

"There are many athletes who have devoted a whole heap of money to charities and have started organizations and schools to help the neglected and needy youth. You know, basketball players Stephon Maubury and Ben Wallace have basketball shoes that sell for twenty dollars. Nothing like the exploitative, rip-off prices of Air Jordan's, and I *must* mention the tennis player, Andre Agassi and his Andre Agassi College Preparatory Academy In 2001 his Charitable Foundation opened the Academy, a K-12 public charter school defined by educational excellence. He established and runs the Academy for underprivileged children."

"All the money those at'letes make all of them should be starting foundations and offering free education including health care. I spend more time beamin' in on talk shows and magazines."

Sometimes the writers of articles show disrespect, like when they called the only Black man on the high court, the Supreme Court of the United States, an Uncle Tom! On the cover of a popular Black Magazine, in November 1993 there was a big picture of Clarence Thomas wid an Aunt Jemima handkerchief on his head."

Pausing as she looked Malcolm directly into his eyes she continued, "And if that wasn't enuff, three years later they show him again on the cover lookin' like a lawn jockey! His face atop a lawn jockey figure!"

Brother Malcolm launched into his teaching, lecture mode. "Sister, sister, those depictions of the man are too kind, too compassionate. That man has done more than any other person Black or White to turn back the clock on civil rights, all the way back to the pre-Civil War lawn jockey days. He is an absolute disgraceful betrayer. The latest Supreme Court decision on school segregation resulted in a 5 to 4 vote in favor of schools not having to consider race in districting and Thomas voted with the retrograde conservative majority."

"You sure are gettin' riled up this morning. First you dancin' and now you preachin'." A gentle breeze met the couple as they rounded a corner of the boulevard that was banked with red, white, and pink azaleas. Sojourner took in their beauty, hesitated then murmured, "Malcolm, Spike Lee was right!"

"Right about what?"

"In this article in EMERGE magazine, 'about Justice Thomas, Spike Lee said, 'Malcolm X, if he were alive today, would call Thomas a handkerchief head, a chicken and biscuit eating Uncle Tom'. And here you are, alive and well in Revolutionary's Retreat doing' just that."

Halting in his pace, running his hand through his hair, and with stiffening shoulders Malcolm spluttered, "Do you know that in Thomas' first two years on the bench, in five major cases involving civil rights and liberties, Thomas voted against minorities every time. He agreed with Anthony Scalia, the most conservative member of the court, over 90% of the time."

"His voting record is mighty poor and he ain't had no business messin' wid that girl, Anita –what's her last name? Nevah mind, you know who I mean, but nevah the less it's disrespectful to call him such insultin' names in public. Ain't like the old times. When I met wid President Lincoln, September 29 of 1864, Mr. Lincoln showed me great respect. He treated me wid more kindness and cordiality then imaginable. He took my little book, Book of Life, and wid the same hand that signed the death warrant of slavery, he wrote, 'For Aunty Sojourner Truth, September 29, 1864, A. Lincoln'"

"Aunty! Was his mother or father your mother's sister? I doubt that. Sister Sojourner. I'm sure that in 1864, meeting with President Lincoln was a great honor. But on another note, we know the primary reason for the Emancipation Proclamation was not to free the slaves. Lincoln sincerely believed that Blacks were inferior to whites and he signed that proclamation to save the nation from dividing itself. NOT to free the slaves. The freeing part was incidental to the occasion and could never be realized. After the Civil War, when the question was asked, 'What should be done for the Negroes?', Lincoln thought about colonizing the freedmen on the island of Vache off the coast of Haiti. And if you want further proof, ask Br. Carter G. Woodson."

12

Sojourner staunchly and vigorously replied, "Incidental or not, it became law and it was our business to see that it was carried out!"

In calm tones Malcolm said, "True, true, but I don't appreciate him calling you Aunty. That familiarity is typical of white folk's arrogance and feelings of superiority. I got a good mind to go over to President's Palace and tell him so."

Sojourner waved her walking stick again, looked at Malcolm sternly, as she said, "You will do no such thing." She stopped, focusing on several cloudlets that super imposed on each other, and with the sunrise behind, created a breathtaking kaleidoscope.

Malcolm too came to a halt and scrutinized his partner's countenance, thinking, 'Sojourner is studying those clouds the way a palmist or tea reader studies palms or tea leaves. I wonder if she can read clouds the way Sister Merriweather in Detroit used to read palms and leaves.'

Sojourner shifted her gaze from the sunrise, whose reflection was turning the boulevard into a glorious rosy shade, to Malcolm. Along the roadway were air-cushioned benches and Sojourner signaled Malcolm to sit. He crossed his long legs and leaned back to listen to his elder.

"Son", she began, "I've been travelin' these roads over 150 years, and I've been lookin' at countries and continents and seen changes in leaders and names and characters and populations and its amazin' how little has changed when it comes to mankind being considerate of humankind."

Malcolm wondered what differentiation she was making between mankind and humankind but remained quiet.

"Now take the USA, for example, been over 200 years since the Constitution was written by a group of mostly wealthy, white men. And who's runnin' the country today? -a group of wealthy, white men. There's a paltry number of wimmin and Blacks in the

Congress and one Black man and one white wimmin on the Supreme Court. There should be farmers who do real farm work, in the Senate. There should be factory workers, welfare mothers, nurses, let those people have a real say in makin' the laws. Those White men who wrote the Constitution had good intentions but not for all."

"Wealthy white men and most of them slave owners", Malcolm interjected.

Sojourner continued as if uninterrupted. "Constitution talks 'bout rights for all. If there was equal rights for all, then why we need such things like equal rights amendments, wimmin's rights, prisoner's rights, chilluns rights. As long as people have so much greed in them, takin' what rightfully belongs to others, - the country, the world will stay in turmoil. It's avarice and greed. One group of people actually takin' the land from one country taking the very earth out of another country; America took and stole the land from the Native American Indians. Do you know what the geography of the USA would look like if the Native Americans took back all the land that America took from them? Be a big empty space round the Southeast section, a great big hole. And I've seen Black folks lose millions of acres in the South."

"LOSE their land!" Malcolm sat up and exploded. "It's not that they couldn't FIND their land or they didn't know where it disappeared to. No, their land was stolen, robbed from them by crooks operating within the law, - cheated out of their land by chicanery and deceit."

"Now listen here, it's a beautiful, peaceful morning. Just listen to the birds chirpin' and singin' to one another and you exploding so loud the birds will stop their singin' and what kind of heaven would we have?"

Leaning back on the bench he let out a long sigh. "You know, Sister, it's a shame. In 1914, Blacks owned 14 million acres of

14

land in the South. In 1960, only 10 million and today, I'll wager less than 4 million."

"Be patient son, and let me finish my thought. As I was saying, I've seen wars and rebellions, and revolutions; men takin' what ain't theirs and using force, falsification, and whatevah to be the most powerful. The earthlings need to put more of the old fashion Godliness in their lives.

Malcolm lightly stroked his beard before answering. "I don't want to sound disrespectful, but the earth ones are going to need to do more than follow the dictates of their Gods. Recently, Christiane Amanpour, international chief news correspondent for CNN, produced a three-part documentary called "God's Warriors" featuring Jews, Muslims and Evangelical Christians that are all following their God's orders, a remarkable documentary. The Godly orders include terrorizing, influencing political affairs with their religious dogma, intimidating social activities, murdering and driving people off their lands while they claim to be following God's teachings according to their respective religions."

Speaking with finality Sojourner rose from the bench, took Malcolm's arm, and repeated softly: "The true God is missing from the lives of folks. The world functions, operates, however you want to call it, wid the interaction of God, humankind and the cosmos."

"But isn't it up to humankind to struggle and fight for a just world, a world of equality?"

"The earth folks get just what they accept," said Sojourner with finality.

And so they strolled down the Glory Road, arm in arm, and what a pair! No sex or gender inequality here. Two tall, remarkable, fearless personalities with arresting dignity. Their power and genius combined producing a majestic, energy. Undeniably, both had paid their dues, but like the great ones, they still had plenty of reserve and human resources to create new pastures for the goodness of all.

Chapter One Glossary & Endnotes

- *Patrice Lumumba (1925-1961):* Born in the Congo, was the head of the Congolese National Movement, led the movement toward national independence, and the fight against Belgium's colonial rule. A coup allegedly orchestrated by the U.S. dethroned Lumumba and placed Joseph Mobutu in command. Lumumba was assassinated in 1961, reportedly by the Congolese government but reputedly by the U.S. government.

- *Aunt Jemima:* A trademark for pancake flour, syrup and other breakfast foods owned by Quaker Oats. The trademark dates to 1893 and the pancake mix debuted in 1889. The phrase, Aunt Jemima, is sometimes used as the female version of Uncle Tom, to refer to a Black woman perceived as obsequiously servile or acting in a self-deprecating manner in order to please whites. The 'mammy" image of Aunt Jemima remains derogatory.

- *Ben Wallace and Stephon Maubury:* Professional basketball players in the NBA (*National Basketball Association*) in the United States.

- *50 Cents, Trick Daddy, Souljah Boy, Snoop Dogg*: Popular male hip-hop and rap artists in the '90's and 2000's.

- *Ella Baker 1903-1986 aka Fundi (In Kiswahili, "Fundi" is a word for a person who passes on skills to a younger generation)*: She was a lifelong Civil Rights activist. Her greatest asset was her ability to mobilize and organize people of all generations. She was the mentor of SNCC (*Student Nonviolent Coordinating Committee*) and advisor to many of the male leaders of the Civil Rights Movement. The Movement would not have been the same without her.

- *Paul Robeson (1898-1976):* A multi-lingual African-American actor, athlete, bass-baritone concert singer, writer, civil rights activist, Spingarn Medal winner and Stalin Peace Prize laureate. Robeson possessed one of the few true basses in American music and the first to bring spirituals to the concert stage. His open advocacy for the Soviet Union made him a target by critics in the United States and resulted in his being investigated by the FBI under J. Edgar Hoover. In 1950, the State Department denied him a passport and issued a "stop notice" in all ports. From 1950 until the late 1970's, it was difficult if not impossible to hear Robeson on records, radio or see any of his films. In 1976, at the age of 77 Paul Robeson died and was interred in Ferncliff Cemetery in Hartsdale, New York. (*The same resting space of Malcolm X, and Ida H. Joseph, the author's mother*)

- *Arthur Ashe 1943-1993*: Tennis star of the '60's and '70's. First Black man to win the U.S. Open 1968; Australian Open 1970; and Wimbledon 1975, and that year was ranked number one in the world. He was the first Black on the U.S. Davis Cup Team. In 1980 he retired due to a heart ailment that required by-pass surgery. In 1998, he discovered he had AIDS, from an HIV infected blood transfusion during heart surgery in 1983. He made the news public in 1992 and died the next year.

- *Spike Lee:* His birth name is Shelton Jackson Lee. He was born on March 20, 1957 in Atlanta, Georgia. He is an African-American film director, producer, writer, actor, Emmy Award Recipient and Academy Award nominated American Film Director. He is one of the most important young filmmakers and a controversial figure in Black culture.

- *Lincoln's Consideration of Colonizing Freedmen in Haiti—See The African Background Outlined or Handbook for the Study of the Negro* by Carter G. Woodson © 1936

18

Chapter Two
Ida B. Wells' Tea Room

Malcolm and Sojourner approached an intersection with signposts, one pointing North, INSURGENT SISTERS, the other South, TRIBAL NATIONS.

"Which way this morning, Sister?" asked Malcolm.

"Well, when I want to get my blood stirred-up I go by Revolutionary's Retreat community and my blood gets a stirrin' when I hear John Brown, Harriet Tubman, and Frederick Douglass, talkin' bout the victories dey won and the ones dey should have won. If I want poetic inspiration, I pass by Poets Pavilion and catch Langston Hughes, Gwendolyn Brooks, and June Jordan in dialogue. But, when I want to hear drop-dead politics, I visit the Insurgent Sisters. And son, let me tell you, when Nanny the Maroon, Rosa Luxemburg, and Ida B. Wells get together dere ain't a problem they can't solve. So let's head in that direction. You can use some of dere wimmin wise words and wisdom", chuckled Sojourner.

Along the boulevard, a bank of red and white azaleas graced the entrance to the INSURGENT SISTERS domain. The duo slowed their pace to admire the radiant but restful array of flowers leading to the Tea Room. Ida B. Wells continued her tradition of organizing Black woman clubs, by hosting unscheduled debates, discussions, and discourses around women issues.

This morning as she readied her dining facilities, she was engaged in soulful conversation with Viola Liuzzo who was assisting her. Ida B. skillfully maneuvered a plate of blueberry scones from one solar oven shelf to the warming level as she told Viola to arrange the corn muffins in a figure eight style on the plates edged with the blue curly cue design. "I know just what my daily customers appreciate and some of them rarely change from their usual. I've been here since 1931 so I' m familiar with their preferences."

19

Viola was enamored of Ida B. Wells and this morning as she helped prepare the menus her bright, striped, burgandy, stretch shirt with rolled up button cuffs, matched her mood.

"You've been here for decades. I was about three or four years old when you arrived. The work you did for civil rights way back then and your anti-lynching work was incredible. I'm amazed the current generation knows so little about you."

"They know even less about you Viola! You sacrificed your life during the Civil Rights Movement. All of America should remember your name with Goodman, Chaney, and Schwerner, the young civil rights workers, 20, 21 and 24 years young, who were brutally murdered by the Klan in the summer of 1964. Goodman and Schwerner were white volunteers from the North and Chaney a Black youth from the South."

"You were a crusader for justice and women's rights advocate throughout your entire life despite being raised in what Nina Simone in a song, called 'Mississippi Goddamn'", said Viola with emphasis and admiration.

Ida smoothed her crisp, blue apron with white ruffles over her boysenberry check cotton lounger, rested her pan of honey buns on a counter, and fixed empathetic eyes on Viola.

"Let me tell you a bit about my life and you will see the ideological similarities in our lives, and ideologies count more than class, race, and privilege. As you know, I was born in Holly Springs, Mississippi, one of seven children of slaves who were freed after the Civil War. From a young age I took on the responsibility of caring for my younger siblings when both parents and my youngest sibling, a nine-month-old brother, died of yellow fever. I was fourteen at the time. I managed to work my way through Rust College in Holly Springs."

Viola Liuzzo questioned Ida, "You were raising your siblings and still attended college?

"Yes, at the time I didn't consider it anything special. It was important to me to keep the family together, and I simply valued education. To strive for knowledge and equality, was a natural for me. In 1880 I moved to Memphis, Tennessee with all my siblings except my fifteen year old brother, and attended summer sessions at Fisk University in Nashville, Tennessee."

"I know that from 1884 to 1891 you taught in the public schools in Memphis, Tennessee." Viola fingered then tasted one of the honey buns. She licked a drop of honey from her thin, rosy colored lips saying, "Mmm, that's so good. What was it like teaching public school in those days?"

"They were segregated public schools. 'Separate but equal, integrated schools' not back then, my friend, -but at the same time I was writing articles for a Black newspaper, *Free Speech*. The Memphis Board of Education fired me from my teaching job in 1891."

"Let me guess the reason", smiled Viola. "Articles were too controversial, too incendiary, just too much truth for the White establishment."

"You got it just right, sister. But you know I eventually became co-owner and editor of *Free Speech,* which was an anti-segregationist newspaper. Viola, my editorials were so forceful and truthful that they upset the white establishment and believe me, there was enjoyment writing the articles and pleasure in their effect"

"The joys of struggle", commented Viola as she reached for a molasses cookie.

Ida didn't usually taste her pastries, but the way her helper was salivating over those molasses cookies, made her decide to try one. Munching her way through the cookie that was indeed scrumptious, she continued, "I had three friends who owned a grocery store and they were attacked and lynched because they were taking business away from white competitors."

"Lynched." Viola cried out, her eating interrupted by the words.

Nodding her head in both agreement and with sorrowful memories, Ida continued, "I was so enraged, I wrote an article encouraging Blacks to leave Memphis. My words were, 'There is... only one thing left to do: save our money and leave a town which will neither protect our lives or property, nor give us a fair trial in courts, but takes us out and murders us in cold blood when accused by white people.' Many African-Americans left and others organized boycotts of white owned businesses."

Viola said softly, "Yes, I recall that because of that article and other investigative reporting that you did, your newspaper office was ransacked, and you had to leave Memphis."

"Yes, I had to *flee* Memphis for my life, and went to Chicago."

"Your work, research I should say, on lynching documented, and established the fact that Southerners concocted the rape excuse to hide the real reason for lynching Black men which was black economic progress which threatened not only white Southerner's pocketbooks but also their ideas about black inferiority."

Ida B. Wells was prideful but not the least bit arrogant about her accomplishments. "In 1892, I published by pamphlet that became quite famous, *Southern Horrors: Lynch Law in All its Phases.* This was a major parcel in my campaign against lynching. Let me add, in 1895 I published, A Red Record, a statistical treatment of tragic lynching in the United States. I appealed to President William McKinley for support in these words: "nowhere in the civilized world, save in the United States, do men go out in bands of fifty to five thousand, to hunt down, shoot, hang or burn to death, a single individual, unarmed and absolutely powerless."

"And what was his response?"

"It was sufficiently negligible enough to encourage me to continue my relentless crusade. By the way, my speeches were well covered by English newspapers that drew vicious attacks from white newspaper in the United States. Viola, I was militant in my demands for equality and justice for African-Americans and insisted that the African-American must win justice through its own efforts. Then, thankfully, we have White persons like you, Viola Liuzzo. And here we are today, two historical civil rights workers serving up delicious delicacies for our fellow friends and companions."

" Before we resume our servile roles," quipped Viola, "tell me about your role as a self-appointed attorney."

"Oh, you must be referring to the case in Illinois in 1895. Yes, I'm proud of that one. Violence against Blacks was growing and nothing was being done about it. I was investigating a lynching in Cairo, Illinois and the Blacks in the town were too afraid to protest. And I could understand that, but I really couldn't accept it. I went to the State House in Springfield and argued against the reinstatement of the sheriff who had permitted the murder. I pleaded the case against the best lawyers in southern Illinois and won."

"Wow! You were really, truly one grandiose, hell of a woman!" Viola looked at this comely, brown skinned woman, even featured, lips compressed, arched eyebrows over deep intelligent eyes with her natural hair done in an upsweep held in place with pearl studded pins, - and felt waves of adoration sweeping through her body.

The two women broke the pause in their Tea Room preparations but continued their conversation. Viola arranged napkins and utensils in their respective holders and said, "In addition to your anti-lynching activities, your strong will and spirit was obvious in your anti-segregation moves. Few people know that seventy one years before Rosa Parks' historic 'one woman sit down strike', - seventy one years, imagine that, - you protested in a similar way against segregated local railways."

"And even fewer people know that before me there was Sojourner Truth who led a one woman strike against segregated street cars. And please don't ask me why all these solo strikes were initiated by women. Perhaps it was because the laborious work the women did required public transportation and they were just plain tired physically as well as with the daily burdens of racial inequality.

In 1865, streetcars were desegregated by law and Sojourner knew her rights. She had several encounters wherein streetcars would not stop for her. In one incident the conductor tried to throw her off and wrenched her arm. She later had the conductor arrested and convicted of assault and battery. Earlier in 1865, Harriet Tubman was dragged out of her seat on a streetcar and thrown into the baggage car. It took THREE men to throw her out -she was stronger than me.

Let me tell you about an incident. It was in 1884 and a conductor on the Chesapeake, Ohio & South Western Railroads Company - I'll never forget that name, - told me to give up my seat to a white man and ordered me to sit in the smoking or "Jim Crow" car. Well, sister Liuzzo, Sister Wells did not intend to give up her seat to any white person. I sat in that seat until the conductor had to get two other to men help him drag me out of that car. I returned to Memphis and immediately hired an attorney to sue the railroad. I won my case in the local circuit court -won $500.00 for damages, - but the Supreme Court of Tennessee, reversed the lower court's ruling in 1887."

"On what grounds were you suing the Railroad Company?"

"Viola, you see, the federal Civil Rights Act of 1875-which banned discrimination on the basis of race, creed, or color in theatres, hotels, transport and other public accommodation--had just been declared unconstitutional in the Civil Rights Cases (1883), and several railroad companies were able to continue racial segregation of their passengers. In my opinion the Civil Rights Act was the law of the land."

"Sister Ida, there is so much about you that I admire. I remember the stance you took during women's suffrage parades. You refused to stand in the back because you were black. In 1895 when you married Ferdinand L. Barnett, you set an early precedent of keeping your own last name with that of your husband. This was very, very unusual at the time. How did your husband feel about that?"

Ida started checking the aroma from the teas to determine their strengths. The mixture of the scents from the teas was equal to any aromatherapy treatment imaginable. With a deep inhalation, Ida settled on a table height four legged cushioned swivel stool and with a satisfied smile, said, "I met Ferdinand in 1893 when I was searching for a lawyer to settle a libel suit, so he was familiar with my personality. He had to know that I was a strong willed person and he definitely knew that I was a woman whose life's work was fighting injustice and, in the process, setting precedents. So, I guess he wasn't too surprised and realized that marriage didn't rob me of my proclivities for fighting injustices."

Ida's devotee likewise sat on one of the stools and said, "Let me try to sum up Ida B. Wells in one super-superb sentence. You were the most powerful leader in the anti-lynching campaign in America; a suffragette ahead of her time; newspaper editor, publisher and investigative reporter; an important activist in the early Civil rights Movement; co-founder of the NAACP, (National Association for the Advancement of Colored People); a race woman, mother, wife and an outstanding role model for anyone with a heart."

Ida B. laughed as she countered: "Now it's time for your story You're not up here in the Retreat on a hummer."

As a resident in the Insurgent Sisters domain, Viola was one of the youngest, having arrived in 1965 at age 39. She was a housewife and mother of five from Detroit, Michigan. Sitting on her stool in Ida's Tea Room, with a necklace of a colorful menagerie of stone critters and matching earrings, and her near shoulder length

25

slightly wavy brownish hair, her demeanor was resolute. With an unassuming shrug of her shoulders, Viola began speaking softly and slowly.

"The shocking television images of Bloody Sunday - that was the spur for my volunteering to go to Selma. It was on the 7th of March that the civil rights demonstrators began a march from Selma to Montgomery, Alabama. Row after row of helmeted state police, gas masks hanging from their belts and billy clubs clenched in their hands met the demonstrators at the city limits. The commander of the State highway patrol ordered the marchers to turn back, giving them two minutes to comply. My goodness! It was horrendous, ungodly; I had never seen anything like it. In less than two minutes, with the command, 'State Troopers Advance!' the troopers charged into the crowd swinging their clubs, unleashing tear gas and behind the troopers came a wave of Sheriff Clark's posse men mounted and riding ram shod into the retreating marchers."

Viola gave a visible shudder at the thought of clouds of tear gas, bodies pummeled, bloodshed, bones broken and Sheriff Clark shouting, 'get those goddamn niggers'.

"It was indeed a bloody Sunday. As I watched that horror on television along with thousands of other Americans, it was a gigantic stutter step in the road to freedom and democracy."

"How little things change from my time to your, - racism, hatred, ignorance. When will it ever end?" Ida B. puckered her lips, cupped her hand under her chin and said, "Continue with your story, child. It needs to be heard."

"After many discussions and indecisions, a second march from Selma to Montgomery was planned. After the march, the marchers decided to return from Montgomery to Selma as soon as possible. Volunteers with private cars were needed to ferry them back to Selma. I decided to respond to Martin Luther King's request for volunteers, packed my bags, and said my good byes to my family.

I remember telling my husband that 'there are too many people who just stand around talking'. It was a three-day drive and I arrived in time for the march on Thursday, March 25. After listening to Dr. King's 'How Long Will It Take' speech, along with a Black teenager, Leroy Moton, - he was such a neat kid, who helped with the driving, - we drove five passengers to Selma. We turned around to head back to Montgomery in my Oldsmobile to pick up more passengers. I noticed that a car with four Klansmen, on Highway 80 the route of the march, was tailing me. I accelerated to try to out run my pursuers." At this point Viola's stoicism enabled her to continue.

"About halfway between Selma and Montgomery the Klansmen overtook us and I remember shots being fired." Viola arched her eyebrows, pressed her lips together, and looked at Ida stoically."

Ida gently stroked Viola Liuzzo's cheek and affectionately patted her hand. "We made our decisions. We took a position based on our ideologies fueled by energy that comes from a very strong sense of justice and a commitment to struggle for equality and an end to the tragic, horrendous villainous atrocities that the Klansmen and their followers committed on innocent Black men women and children, on courageous white men and women, young, middle- aged and old. I know how very hard it must have been on your five children and husband to lose their mother and wife so tragically. Viola, hear me, we are here in this divine retreat because we responded to a call that we heard and unfortunately too many others did not.

Ida was silent as she recalled Leroy Moton's story: Liuzzo accelerated in an attempt to outrun the pursuers, singing "We Shall Overcome", at the top of her lungs. The Klansmen over took the car and one of them shot her twice in the face as she drove, killing her instantly. The car ran off the road in to a ditch and I pretended to be dead when those murderers, the Klansmen, came to check out the wreck to see if they had accomplished their intentions. One of the Klansmen was an FBI informant and despite information from him, the men who committed the murder were not convicted.

President Johnson, bless his soul, took action that resulted in the three Klansmen being convicted for violating civil rights law and received 15 years in prison.

Ida summed up the episode. "Viola Liuzzo, your death led to the very critical question among the movement, - had non-violence reached its limits as a successful tactic in the struggle? Your death was a sharp wake up call. The struggle had become war."

Thankfully, kudos to Morris Dees, founder of the Southern Poverty Law Center (SPLC). The center wages campaigns against hate groups by suing them in court. In the 1980's and 1990's, the center sued the Ku Klux Klan groups that targeted African-Americans. It was multi-million dollar judgments that forced some of these groups into bankruptcy.

Viola nodded, then shrugged as Ida's words sank in. "These pastries and drinks have heard a bit of history this morning, Ida, and now it's about time for us to satisfy the appetites of your customers." The twosome once again resumed preparations.

Sister Wells was an extremely popular figure in Revolutionary' Retreat and her Tea Room was the Mecca for women. The veranda of her porch was an outdoor café with air cushioned chairs and tables bearing bowls of fresh colorful petunias, pansies, zinnias, African violets and baby roses. In one corner was a stand with a list of teas posted on the newspaper-covered wall. The list read: This Weeks Specials: Lemon grass, Lime leaf, Elder bush, Conga Laura, Wild bush, Lilly root, Bitter payee, Corilah bush, Sweet broom, Minny root, and Sweet jasmine.

Many of the teas were recommendations from the West Indian Island women who swore by the teas' potential for curing ailments. Sister Wells would argue that there ARE no ailments up here. But those wise grannies, the three Queens from St. Croix, Virgin Islands—Queen Mary, Queen Agnes and Queen Matilda, leaders of the Fireburn Labor Rebellions in 1878, and Nanny the Maroon from Jamaica, informed Ida that the reason folks ARE so healthy up here was due to the diets that they, the grannies, had brought with them.

Next to the tea rack was an assortment of cakes and buns and a rack of cigars, pipes, and tobaccos. The latter was non-poisonous, nicotine free. The rarified air purified it. The Native American Indians chiefs, Geronimo, Joseph, and Tecumseh, frequent visitors to the veranda, had carried peace pipes and tobacco along the Milky Way to the Spirit World and donated them to Ida's veranda. For those with a sweet tooth there were honey buns, molasses cookies, blue berry muffins, and custard tarts. For a plainer taste you could choose from Johnnycakes, corn bread, fry dough or pan bread. A solar oven kept the bakery goods warm and fresh.

Already a diversified group of women occupied the veranda. Around a medium-sized white lace covered table with a purple ceramic bowl in its center filled with African violets, sat Zora Neale Hurston, Lorraine Hansberry, Raya Dunayevskaya, and Audre Lorde. At a nearby butcher-block table for two sat Anna Mae Aquash, a Native American activist and Lillian Ngoyi, a leader of the women's protest against the carrying of passes in South Africa.

Lorraine and Audre and Zora together claimed triple residency in Poets' and Playwrights' Pavilion and Gay Gardens but, insisted that they belonged to the Insurgent Sisters Cloud Range as well. The women on the veranda were indeed a splendid sight. Each arrived on the Glory Road wearing the clothes of their time so you always saw multi-generational wardrobes. Some of the older ones liked to adopt the latest fashions so it wasn't uncommon to see, for example, Mary McLeod Bethune-Cookman, educator and founder of Bethune-Cookman College, wearing a trendy shawl-collared, button less plaid jacket, with patch pockets and a calf length turquoise colored skirt. Zora, whose clothing defied classification, was wearing a tangerine jump suit with brass buttons on the pockets and cuffs. Audre was stunning in an African kente cloth dress.

29

Zora sat quietly puffing on a corncob pipe and sipping lemon grass tea, listening to Lorraine and Raya, in sympathy with one another, as they talked about the current women's movement that failed to incorporate race and class in its conception. Audre was nodding in agreement, as she savored a honey bun and custard tart with a frosty glass of ginger beer in reserve.

Lillian Ngoyi and Anna Mae Aquash dressed in clothes of their cultures were arguing the merits of elder bush tea for morning or evening usage. On a wall next to their table was a quilt designed by the older women of the Women of Color Quilted Network, the Columbus, Ohio chapter. It was a special gift to Ida from Florynce Kennedy, a witty, flamboyant activist, well known for her statement, "If men could get pregnant, abortion would be a sacrament."

On a love seat with the quilt as a backdrop, in their attractive well-tailored aviator uniforms sat Bessie Coleman and Amelia Earhart, once again rehashing their lives and flights as first popular female aviators of their race. Bessie Coleman, born in 1892, in Atlanta, Texas, the tenth of thirteen children still maintained her trim athletic figure. Amelia, also fit and slender was born in1897, in Atchison, Texas. She had one sibling, a younger sister, who during childhood followed Amelia in adventurous activities collecting squiggly creatures, climbing trees and on snowy days 'belly slamming' on her sleigh.

This morning as Bessie and Amelia studied Ida's calligraphy describing her delicacies, Bessie asked, "Amelia, I wonder when Ida had time to learn calligraphy? I barely had time to learn how to read and write. At the age of six I had to walk four miles daily to get to the all Black school."
Bessie re-adjusted her bluish gray pilot's cap with the initials B.C on either side of the gold eagle insignia and smiling in Amelia's direction continued, "Meanwhile, my dear friend, you were receiving home schooling from your mother and a governess and had a large at home library at your disposal."

"Here we were, just five years differences between our ages and at age nine you were caring for your three younger sisters and managing the household while your mother worked as a cook and house keeper. I had schooling at my doorstep, but I wasn't a very good student. I'd rather be outdoors hunting rats with a rifle." Amelia picked up one of the cobalt blue half filled water glasses on the small table in front of the divan and admired the resplendent reflection cast by the sunrays. It reminded her of beautiful sunrises and sunsets she had experienced. Thoughtfully she said, "We had many differences Bessie, but what we had in common was a love of flying and a strong commitment to do so."

Bessie waved the blue trimmed papyrus menu back and forth as she explained, "Talk about differences during my early childhood I played outdoors during the week and on Sundays went to church, but as I grew older I had to help my mother in the garden and with household chores. But at cotton harvest time, Meeley let me tell you, each man, woman, boy, and girl were out in those fields picking cotton, picking cotton, picking cotton. And I don't want to hear any nonsense like hard work, discipline and responsibilities strengthened my character. It was nothing short of child abuse and violation of child labor laws but laws of those kinds didn't apply to Black folks."

"Where was your father and older siblings at the time you were surrogate mother?"

"My father left for Oklahoma in 1901 frustrated by the racial barriers in Texas and my mother and older siblings decided not to go with him. Shortly after he left, my older brothers also left home."

Amelia chimed in, "My father was no paragon of virtue. He was an alcoholic and practically drained the family funds. Our economic stability was based on the wealth of my maternal grandfather. Our family moved quite a bit and I didn't attend public school until I was 12 and in the seventh grade. I graduated high school, started junior college, but never finished."

31

Momentarily distracted by the medium size, Cleopatra butterfly with its various yellow shades, Amelia watched it settle on the edge of the table, folding its wings upright over its back. In soft tones, "Bessie, butterflies and birds, - they're natural flyers, instinctive, - you and I had to go to schools and learn through taking many lessons. For me a ten minute flight in Long Beach, California, in 1920 was the inspiration for my future in flying."

"As for me, after a term in the Colored Agricultural and Normal University in Langston, Oklahoma, I ran out of money and returned to Texas and worked as a laundress. I knew laundering was not going to be my life's work. At age 23, I moved to Chicago to live with my brothers and got a job as a manicurist in a barbershop. The pilots who were returning home from World War I told stories about flying in the war. I, fantasizing, determined to be a pilot. At the barbershop I met several influential men from the Black community, including Robert S. Abbott, founder and publisher of the *Chicago Defender*, and Jesse Binga, a real estate promoter. I received financial backing from Binga and the *Chicago Defender.* Meeley, I could not find anyone to teach me. American flight schools wouldn't admit me because I was Black and a woman. The Black aviators wouldn't train me either. Robert Abbott, a true supporter, encouraged me to study abroad and I prepared myself to attend aviation school in France. I'll never forget my departure for France in November 1920, what an adventure! I completed a ten months course in seven months at the Ecole d'aviation des Frères Caudon at Le Crotoy in the Somme. I was something else, you should have seen me."

Bessie stood up, her toothsome smile dominating her smooth, round baby like face and began moving her body and arms in imitation of her descriptions. "My learning included 'tailspins, banking, and looping the loop'. I received my license on June 15, 1921, at age 29. I was the first Black woman to earn a license from the prestigious FAI (*Federation Aeronautique Internationale*), and the only woman of the sixty-two candidates to earn FAI license during that time. How about that!"

Bessie resumed her seat and she and Amelia raised and clicked their glasses with Amelia gaily saying, "Hear, hear!"

Relishing in the memories of her accomplishments Bessie continued, with a sparkle in her dark, almond shaped eyes, "I spent three additional months in France before departing for New York, September 1921, and surprisingly enough I was greeted by press coverage. Imagine me, the Black daughter of sharecroppers with 8th grade schooling, and one term at the Colored Agricultural and Normal University in Oklahoma, becoming a pilot. I made a second trip to France in 1922 to take advanced training for flying as entertainment."

Amelia pushed back her skull type aviator's cap that gave her a debonair look and remarked, "After my initial ten minute flight with Frank Hawks I knew I had to fly and saved up $1000.00 for flying lessons. Bessie, to get to my lessons after taking a bus I had to walk four miles to reach the airfield and that was in January 1921. You walked four miles to elementary school and I walked four miles for flying lessons. There must be something in numerology that unites us. Six months after lessons, I bought a second-hand bright yellow Kinner Airster biplane and flew it to an altitude of 14,000 feet. That set a world record for women pilots. In May 1923 three years after you, I became the 16th woman to be issued a pilot's license by the Federation Aeronautique Internationale."

The women aviators truly loved re-living their flying experiences and sat quietly for a while, finishing their glasses of water. "Let's re-fill our glasses but this time with our favorite cooled Conga Laura tea," suggested Amelia.

As she leaned over to reach her glass, Bessie viewed the small scar on Amelia's cheek. Amelia had served as a nurse during World War I and in 1918 during the Spanish flu epidemic working in Toronto, she contracted flu, pneumonia, and severe sinusitis. The latter resulted in a chronic condition that required periodic drainage. A small drainage tube had been inserted in her cheek leaving a permanent scar. It definitely did not detract from her youthful, attractive looks.

"Meeley, we sure had a lot in common. I had an ardent desire to open a school for aviators and you were instrumental in the formation of The Ninety-Nines, an organization for women pilots. We were both women advocates" and with a little smirk she continued, "publicized in a manner that really belied our abilities. Imagine me, in my military style suit and eloquent speaking style, wooing my audiences, defying racial and gender barriers, stunt flying around the country and billed as 'the world's greatest woman flyer'." Bessie crossed her legs and placed her hands behind her neck, reveling in past glories.

"It's a shame that we didn't get together before meeting on the Glory Road", lamented Amelia. "The great color divide kept us apart. You were stellar in your refusal to perform unless the audiences were desegregated and everyone attending used the same gates. As the first woman to fly solo across the Atlantic Ocean, I was the first woman to receive the Distinguished Flying Cross, but I regret not being an activist for Black equality as I was for women's equality. After I married publicist and book publisher George P. Putnam, I retained my independence and referred to the marriage as a "partnership" with "dual control" but I should have done much more for Civil Rights."

"Amelia, in retrospect, yes," Bessie agreed. "We were unusual women. Think about it, our very departure from earth was unusual. I died in a plane crash in 1926 at age 34 doing what I loved best, exhibition stunt flying. I remember the day clearly, -April 30, 1926 giving an exhibition for the Jacksonville, Florida Negro Welfare League, - 7:30 P.M. flying at 110 miles per hour at an altitude of 3,500 feet I put my plane into a 1,500 foot nose dive and never came out." With a distinct exhaling, she continued, "And you along with your navigator, Frank Noonan, disappeared over the central Pacific Ocean, near Howland Island during an attempt to circumnavigate the globe in 1937, at age 40. Meeley, the U.S government spent $4 million dollars and your husband spent millions searching for you and here you are sitting on this love seat with aviatrix Bessie Coleman." Both women gave mirthless laughs.

Earhart commented to Bessie, "Those earth folks know so little about you Bessie, and when it comes to me, the most popular conversation is my disappearance. All sorts of theories exist since there is no proof of my fate." With a wry smile she added, "If they are so damn interested why don't they just ask me? I can put to rest all the theories about my disappearance, just ask me."

Bessie's retort was, "Cause there's '*No Telephone To Heaven*'. You know that's the title of a book written by Michelle Cliff, a brilliant American-Jamaica author. The earth folks will suffer in puzzlement until they can 'dial-up' or have a website to heaven." The compatible twosome smiled at one another as they checked out Ida's Daily Specials and decided to order lemon meringue tarts to go with the Conga Laura tea.

In a corner of the tearoom around an oblong table with a red-checkered tablecloth were Mother Jones, Emma Goldman, Rosa Luxemburg, and Annie Stein. Comfortably settled on rattan chairs with cushions of the same-checkered pattern, they enjoyed just sitting.

Ida B. was replenishing the tea rack as Fannie Lou Hamer with her noticeable limp, sauntered into the room, and standing hipshot, took in the entire scene with one glance. "Well, well", she said, "and a good 'morning to all. Ida, that corn bread smells mighty good, but what's that segregation table you got over there? As hard as I worked, knocking down chairs and people to hold on to the Mississippi Freedom Democratic party's seat at the national convention in 1964s, and all that marching and jail time I did, and just look at all those white wimmin segregatin' themselves. Guess I'll have to integrate it myself." With a smile and readjusting her straw field hat from her sharecropping days, she went over to join Mother Jones and company. Before she reached their table she called back to Ida, "Sister Ida, you are still very popular down below. I just read about two new books being published about you and one of them is around 400 pages."

Ida with an impish smile retorted, "Any book about me with over 400 pages got to be repetitious, fictitious, or boring. Fannie, go on about your integration business with your bad self."

Turning to Viola, Ida said, "Fannie Lou Hamer was born in 1917 the youngest of twenty children of sharecropper parents. For years, she attributed that limp to childhood polio but later she discovered that it was due to broken bones in childhood that were neither properly diagnosed nor treated. She became a mainstay in the Civil Rights Movement at age 44. Fannie was a revolutionary of the first order. During the voter registration drive, she sacrificed her job as a plantation timekeeper, defying her boss who told her she would lose her job and move out if she tried to register to vote. She was one of many small independent farmers who risked whatever they had to establish civil rights movements in their communities."

Mother Jones who enjoyed bantering with anyone, said, "Fannie Lou, you must think you're Rosa Parks, Gloria Richardson, and Daisy Bates all rolled into one. I don't want to start a protest movement to allow white wimmin the right to sit together if they want to."

Mother Jones at age eighty-three was a leader in the textile workers' strike 1913. The workers were up against the Rockefeller interests, but that did not deter Mother Jones. There were eleven and twelve year old children working in the mills. Mother Jones led them on a march on a hay wagon, from Pennsylvania to Oyster bay, New York where President Theodore Roosevelt was on summer vacation. They stood outside the resort in vain with signs that said, "We Want Time to Play." In one of her public speeches she said, "Our country doesn't kill our children outright, they kill them on the installment plan."

Fannie Lou's reply was, "Mother Jones, let me enjoy my integrated morning breakfast before y'all strike for segregated rights."

As Malcolm and Sojourner approached the tearoom, Ida called out a cheery greeting. The other women looked up and responded with a chorus of salutations.

"Sister Wells," began Sojourner, "it sure is pleasurable to pass your quarters 'cause there's always good food and drink and tobacco so healthy that you can smoke a pipe with no worryin' 'bout--now what's that earth one's name, General 'Spector, Sergeant General? Whatever he's called warnin' people 'bout not smokin'."

"No one bothered to offer Sojourner the correct name, Surgeon General. They were well aware of her trick of baiting people into correcting her so she could come back with a witty response. Ida addressed Malcolm and Sojourner informing them that there would be a special gathering this evening, a forum of sorts."

"Forum? For what? About what?" questioned Sojourner.

Without batting an eyelash, Zora, in her black felt hat slouched at a rakish angle, leaned back in her chair, and wryly commented between sips of lemon grass, "This evening's topic is Feminism vs. Marxism, as related to Homosexuality vs. Capitalism as Related to Sexism vs. Communism, within the Context of an Impending Nuclear Holocaust."

The laughter that followed was mixed with comments. Anna Mae said, "Now Zora, leave them academics be."

"They could hold an entire forum just deconstructing the topic," added Lorraine.

"God don't like ugly", reminded Sojourner.

Lillian Ngoyi with her colorful plaid wool blanket draped around her shoulders, still strong, still unbroken, smiled as she spoke, "The topic is about an all-people's movement for 2008, and I do mean ALL people. I look forward to the day when my people can share the wealth of lovely South Africa." Her life was one of hardships and poverty. She was a religious woman believing in prayer but realizing that change can take place only through action, not meditation, or prayer- but through action. She joined the ANC Women's League in 1952 and was elected president the following year. In March 1980, at the age of 68, she died after a short illness. Over two thousand mourners of all races attended her funeral, which lasted four hours. They came from all over South Africa to Soweto. Her horse drawn coffin was draped in the black, gold and green colors of the ANC and she was laid to rest in the Avalon cemetery as the singing became louder and the ANC salutes the clenched fists, were given.

Raya embraced Lillian's comment and interjected seriously, "If you want to have a successful historical movement for total liberation, it MUST involve all people. There is no such thing as Black history that is not also white history. There is no such thing as women's history that is not the actual history of humanity's struggle toward freedom."

"I'll need another cup of Conga Laura, which is good for clearing up the stomach and the nerves, to help digest those righteous words of Raya's."

"I'll get it for you, Lillian. I can use another cup myself," said Anna Mae as she went to the tea stand.

Sojourner and Malcolm settled down at one of the tables with a flowering pot of dwarfed zinnias under a hand crocheted blue linen tablecloth. They decided to enjoy a bit of refreshment before continuing their morning stroll.

Chapter Two Glossary & Endnotes

- *Raya Dunayevskaya (1910-1987):* A brilliant Russian born intellectual and political analyst and founder of the body of ideas of Marxist-Humanism in the United States. She was the first to develop the theory of state-capitalism and worked out the philosophy of Marxist-Humanism both as global concept and as it is rooted in the United States in labor, the Black dimension and women's liberation.

- *Anna Mae Aquash (aka) Anna Mae Pictou (1945-1975):* Born in Nova Scotia, Canada, a Native American, Mikmaq activist who during the '70's became one of the most active and prominent female member of the American Indian Movement (AIM). She was a main target of the government. Her death, a murder, was a notorious cover up and during her autopsy in a nefarious act of contempt by enemy agents, her hands were cut off. She remains a martyr to her people.

- *Mother Jones (1837-1930):* Birth name - Mary Harris Jones. Born in Cork City, Ireland, her family migrated to the United States in 1848. In 1862, she married George Jones, a member of the Iron Workers Union. She joined the Knights of Labor, a predecessor to the Industrial Workers of the World (IWW or "Wobblies.") As a union organizer she became prominent for organizing the wives and children of striking workers. She became known as "the most dangerous woman in America." Mother Jones remained a union organizer for the UMW affairs almost until her death. She was known to working folk as *"The Miner's Angel."* Her determination was expressed in her famous declaration, "Pray for the dead and fight like hell for the living."

- *Emma Goldman (1869- 1940):* A Russian born, (*Republic of Lithuania*), to Orthodox Jewish parents. She migrated to the United States in 1885 and worked in a clothing factory. She was a fiery dominant anarchist. A writer and lecturer she was lionized as a free-thinking rebel woman. She was imprisoned and deported for her radical activities in the U.S. She was adopted by the 2nd wave of feminism.

- *Annie Stein (1913-1981):* An American political activist and freedom fighter, a consistent worker and organizer for many national and international committees oriented toward the eradication of injustice and oppression. Her most brilliant campaign was her fight to have the Legislative Assembly enacted laws of 1872 and 1873 which made it a crime for certain designated places of public accommodation- hotels, restaurants, theatres, barbershops- to refuse to serve on account of race or color, with the provision that anyplace which was convicted of that crime would lose its license to do business for one year. She formed an organization to see that these laws were enforced and enlisted Mrs. Mary Church Terrell age 86, then the most revered Black woman in America. In 1953, the U.S. Supreme Court issued its' decision. It unanimously decided that the laws of 1872 and 1873 were valid and should be enforced.
- *Rosa Luxemberg (1871- 1919):* An outstanding Polish-born leader of the Socialist Movements in both Poland and Germany. She was a brilliant intellectual who made significant contributions to Marxist theory.

Chapter III

Native Americans: Ghost Riders in the Skies

Malcolm and Sojourner left Ida's Tea Room and took the long way round to the Native American community. The housing units unlike others consisted of a variety of living accommodations. Each tribe's particular living arrangements were based on their past geographic locations and ancestral life styles. There were long houses, tepees, pueblos, wigwams, and modern two-story buildings. Many of the community preferred outdoor living and sleeping in the wide-open campgrounds under the glorious galaxies.

Sojourner and Malcolm admired the carved sign at the entrance, HAPPY HUNTING GROUNDS. A solitary figure was stationed in front of a lodge. Who other than Sanapia, a Comanche shaman, could sit with such alert calmness? She was an Eagle doctor, a title given a shaman who gets power from the Eagle. From age fourteen Sanapia engaged in intense training in herbal and other native doctoring techniques.

Her body motionless beneath her colorful beaded dress she greeted the duo in her own language. With a slight movement of her head, she nodded in the direction of the North and said that the riders were returning. Sojourner mentally recalled the ultra keen audio and kinesthetic senses that Sanapia possessed— she heard sounds in layers. Sojourner was not surprised when she heard the rhythmic, thundering, steady cadence of galloping hooves. Through a blur of dusty rimmed cumulus, clouds appeared the magnificent "ghost riders of the skies." The Native American members of Revolutionary's Retreat were returning from a voyage across the many miles of cloudland. And what a majestic ensemble in their splendid regalia, astride their palominos, dappled grays, pintos and sleek black steeds, all with well-coifed mane, reining in their horses with ease and assuredness.

Leading the riders were Geronimo and Siki Toclanni, a Mescalero Apache woman warrior in Geronimo's guerilla army. She fought alongside Geronimo until the final surrender in 1886. Other riders included Crazy Horse the great Sioux warrior chief, abreast with Dull Knife; Chief Joseph, Nez Perce with two braids framing his regal, noble visage; Chief Sitting Bull with his leather- like skin with fine lines and eyes wiser than his age, a tribal leader who refused to be driven from the Black Hills and took up arms against the whites. He was known for his excellent singing voice as well as for his deeds. Cochise, Chiricahua, Apache, with a large muscular frame and classical features, wore his long black hair in traditional Apache style. Along with Geronimo, the renegade with the very colorful life style was one of the most famous Apache leaders to resist the Mexicans and Americans during the 19th century.

Riding proud and definitely not side saddle, were female warriors: Mary Crawler, aka Moving Robe, reputed to be the only Native American woman who fought at Little Big Horn June 25-26, 1876, in Montana when a mighty alliance of the Sioux Nation defeated the American General Custer; Sarah Winniemucca, Paiute leader and out spoken critic of the treatment of Native Americans by the U.S. government; Running Eagle, a member of the Piegan tribe of the Black Feet Native American Nation, a skilled warrior and buffalo hunter; and Minnie Hollow Wood, Sioux, the only woman of her tribe to wear a war bonnet which she earned in combat against the U.S. Calvary.

The bonnet, also called headdress was a military decoration developed by the Plains Indians. The eagle was considered as the greatest and most powerful of all birds and therefore the finest bonnets were made out of its feathers. In the old days, it was only worn on special occasions and was highly symbolic. Its real value was in its power to protect the wearer. The bonnet was also the mark of highest respect because it could never be worn without the consent of the leaders of the tribe. Feathers were notched or decorated to designate an event and told individuals stories such as killing, scalping, capturing an enemy's weapon and shield and whether the deed had been done on horseback or foot. A chief's war bonnet is worn in high honor. It is comprised of feathers received for good deeds to his community. Each feather is a good deed.

The riders, after tethering, watering and feeding their horses entered the powwow grounds and headed for an area where delicious aromas, -vegetarian, flesh, fowl, honey, pudding - wafted amidst the earthenware bowls, gourds, pots and platters that were set out on roughly hewn tables. Invited to join in the feast, Malcolm and Sojourner willingly accepted. The riders and others replenished their bellies and souls with healthy servings of a concoction of corn soup, rich with venison, caribou, beans, and squash. There was also wild rice, sunflower seeds, and fry bread and jalapeno blue corn muffins. As a special delicacy, there was Blackfoot Pudding. Using the very end of animal intestines, the colon, wash it real good and tie one end shut then stuff the piece with dried berries and a little water and tie the other end. Boil this all day, until it is tender and you have Blackfoot Pudding.

Another delicacy served was a beeate that is prepared from caribou only. It is a kind of haggis, made with blood, a good quantity of fat, shredded tender of flesh, together with the heart and lungs cut or torn into slivers, all of which is put in the stomach of the caribou and toasted by being suspended on a string over a fire. For beverages, there was spring water and non-alcoholic firewater.

Malcolm, smiling with pleasure over the scrumptious soup managed between spoonfuls to say, "Brothers and sisters, this dish should be packaged or canned and sold to the folks below."

Running Eagle, selecting her words with care responded. "White historians generally describe us as nomadic people surviving by hunting, fishing, and berry pickers. You know the classic hunters and gatherers. Yes, we did hunt and we did fish but we also tilled the soil, planted, harvest and stored. Eighty per cent of the garden vegetables used today around the world had been selected and domesticated by native people of Americas before Columbus' so-called discovery in 1492."

"I'd say that most people in America don't know that and many more facts about the first inhabitants of what Americans so boldly call *their country*."

"Brother Malcolm, that's the purpose of this gathering", continued Running Eagle. "Author, writer, and film maker, Toni Cade Bambara is coming over from Writers community to help us record our stories and it won't be a made for television sitcom or a reality show. Gertrude Simmons Bonnin, our writer in residence, as we call her, will play an active role in recording our stories. Zitkala-Sa was so busy with her relentless lobby and lecturing for promoting Native American causes that she neglected her writing. She and Toni will make sure that the film is accountable to our community and not pandering to Eurocentric ideals. The mission of the Ghost Riders will be a central part of the film."

The Ghost Riders had traveled across cirrus, cirrocumulus, alto strata, altocumulus and stratus clouds, gathering signatures for their petition. The petition **demanded** that the United States Government, the Treasury, **remove** Andrew Jackson's face from the twenty-dollar bill!

Suzette La Flesche Tibbles, aka Bright Eyes, chimed in, "It is shameful, a disgrace to honor a man who committed such a heinous act! It was Andrew Jackson, the 7th president of the United States who signed the order in 1838 to remove the Five Civilized Tribes from their territories by force!" Bright Eyes had been a vigorous crusader for Native American land and treaty right. Her small frame bristled her voice trembled as she fingered the ribbons of her cloche bonnet.

"That forced removal, the trek across miles of rough and dangerous terrain, sixteen thousand men, women, and children surrounded by the U.S. Army suffered beyond imagination. At least four thousand of them died— nearly a quarter of the Nation. Jackson's Indian removal act and the forced relocation of the Cherokee Nation to Indian Territory represents one of America's darkest periods. When the survivors arrived, there were hardly any

44

children and very few elders. The removal is aptly referred to as *The Trail of Tears*. It was a ruthless destruction of the future and the past of a people. And he is honored on a twenty-dollar bill. Scandalous!"

Her voice lowered as she folded her hands in the lap of her homespun gray woolen dress. Memories of The Trail of Tears, the suffering from sickness, the heat, the mud, the cold, -the Cherokees from the Southeast being driven from their homeland to a spot in Oklahoma- brought a flood of tears and anger.

Gertrude Simmons Bonnin, aka, Zitkala-Sa, or Red Bird, was brought up as a Yankton Sioux in South Dakota until she was eight years old when she left the reservation to attend a Quaker missionary school. Zitkala-Sa was an exceptionally gifted writer and her autobiographical writings speak with passion and forcefulness of her Indian childhood. Turning to Bright Eyes, Red Bird spoke, her voice edged with remorse, regret, and enmity, "The paleface stole our lands and forced us away. ...we traveled many days and nights, driven like a herd of buffalo... many were sick and ailing. I remember my mother's words about the death of my sister and how she shrieked with pain during that trek. She was feverish, lips parched and dry, hoarse with crying, her throat red and so swollen that she could not drink water. The first night when we reached the western country she died. The Great Spirit had abandoned us and the paleface; they were all a sickly sham!"

Running Eagle picked up the impassioned conversational trend adding, "Sacred homelands, the buffalo and most of all, freedom and independence were stolen from us, America's first citizens. Treaty after treaty, promise after promise was broken. The white man spoke with forked tongue. They established Indian Reservations to "get rid" of America's 'Indian problem'. We a fiercely independent people were condemned to a confined life on desolate land often far from our traditional and sacred homelands. Today, on reservations throughout the country, too many of our descendants still live in poverty, isolation and deprivation with alcoholism, and suicide among our youth at an alarmingly high rate, and all of this is a direct result of broken promises."

Sojourner murmured, "Bright Eyes Running Eagle, Zitkala-Sa, my heart is with you."

At this moment Toni Cade Bambara arrived, an outline of the script in hand, black beret set at a saucy angle, kente cloth scarf thrown loosely around her neck and shoulders and speaking in respectful tones asked the ensemble if they were ready to roll. Sacajawea declared herself the first assistant to Sister Toni because she was well experienced with the Whiteman's arrogance.

The story of Sacajawea and her role in the Lewis and Clark expedition remains an historical combination of fact and legend. There are many stories and claims as to who Sakakawea was. (Sakakawea is the spelling used by Native Americans.) What is known is that she played an important role in the Lewis and Clark voyage to the West and back and they respected her. It is reasonably well accepted that she was from the Mandan and Hidatsa Tribe of the Upper Missouri river. One legend says that she came from the Awaxia people who were under the general tribe name Hidatsa. As the story goes, the Hidatsa men were out hunting when the Shoshone raided their village and Sakakawea and her brother were taken captive and raised by the Shoshone. It was told that Sakakawea was old enough to remember where she came from and as time went by with the help of an old woman, she escaped and found her way back to the village of her people. One of the elders recalls remembering the young woman who was married to the French trapper Charbonneaux and the woman called Sakakawea.

Another legend also states that she was from the Hidatsa tribe and had a younger brother. As this legend goes at age 18, her father gave her to a white man whom she married. His name was Sharbonish and they lived among the Mandans and Hidatsas and had several children (*Sharbonish is the same French trapper Charbonneaux.*) That same year, so he story goes, the two left the

46

lodge, went far away, and traveled far to the west. That was the year before the white party of Lewis and Clark came among the Indians and stayed at Fort Mandan during the winter. They selected Sakakawea and Sharbonish to guide them through that same territory that Sakakawea had been the year before in 1804 and knew that country well. According to this story in 1806, the party passed a camp of the Crow Indians and located her brother there.

Sakakawea's death as reported by Bull's Eye, her grandson, goes as follows:

'Sakakawea was on a trip to a trader's place with two wagons with oxen hitched to them to get coffee. Her daughter and grandson were with her. During the night I was awaken by shooting. Some enemy attacked the camp. My mother said to my grandmother, "Take the child to the willow gulch. So Sakakawea took me by the arm and we ran to the bush. After the firing died down my grandmother took me back to the wagons. My mother was sitting up against the wheel of one of the wagons. I remember it well. She had been badly wounded and was dying. She told my grandmother to take me to the trader's place. We walked over the hills and prairies to the traders' store. My grandmother, Sakakawea, had been hit in the side by a bullet but never said anything. She died at the trader's place from her wounds several days after that time. And that is believed to be the true story of Sakakawea's death.'

Sacajawea alone knew the true story of her life and promised herself that she would eventually reveal it to her heavenly friends. For the present she would let the earth historians and chronologists mix fact and fiction and create legends to satisfy their laborious research. During the meeting, she would make sure that she would set the record straight on any discussion concerning Lewis and Clark. In actuality, Lewis and Clark were no big deal to the Indians. They had seen and been among traders and trappers long before Lewis and Clark. In addition, Lewis and Clark simply could not understand the interactions among families and the responsibilities of the members of the various clans and society. Therefore, how could they pass on valid information about the tribes they met?

Sacajawea and Toni began discussing the script with the community members. The documentary would open with several verses from, "How can one sell the air?" The manifesto of an Indian Chief (*author and source unknown*)*

"How Can One Sell the Air?"

> *The White Chief says that*
> *Big Chief in Washington*
> *sends us greetings of friendship*
> *and good will*
> *This is kind of him for we know*
> *he has little need of our*
> *friendship in return.*
> *His people are many.*
> *They are like the grass*
> *that covers vast prairies.*
> *My people are few.*
> *They resemble the scattering trees*
> *of a storm-swept plain*
>
> *"The Great and I presume*
> *good White Chief sends us word*
> *that he wishes to buy our lands*
> *but is willing to allow us*
> *enough to live comfortably.*
> *We shall consider your offer*
> *to buy our land.*
> *What is it that the White Man*
> *wants to buy*
> *my people will ask.*
> *It is difficult for us to understand.*
>
> *How can one buy or sell the air,*
> *the warmth of the land?*
> *That is difficult for us to imagine,*
> *If we don't own the sweet air*
> *And the bubbling water,*
> *How can you buy it from us?*

Sister Toni spoke in all seriousness to the gathering, "These poetic words are part of a much longer speech that underlies the major divide, the total disconnect, the vast contrasts between the white man's philosophies of the environment and ownership and the Native American's. We know that the concept of ownership of the environment was foreign to the Native Americans. These differences coupled with the might and capitalistic greed of the Europeans led to the destruction and near annihilation of your great Native American tribes."

She bit her lower lip slightly as she gazed at Chief Joseph, Chief Sitting Bull Chief Crazy Horse, and Geronimo who were sitting proudly in a row on one of the hand-hewn benches on the side of the room. Noting their silent approval her face melted with satisfaction.

Siki Toclanni the Apache woman warrior in Geronimo's guerilla warfare stood up with her buffalo cape and an exquisitely colorful beaded necklace and waited to be recognized. After receiving a nod from the assistant director, she spoke, "The dramatization of the Trail of Tears I understand is the next part of the script. In an earlier talk, it was decided that Chief Joseph would narrate it with roles played by various members of the community. That part of the script has not been changed has it?"

With her characteristic impish smile Toni responded, "Not a single change has been made. Chief Joseph is the main man - that is, the narrator, in this segment."

Body and facial expressions of agreement were felt throughout the room.

Toni was seated at the side of the room with Sacajawea right next to her. Rising from her seat Toni in her black suede pants and two-inch heel boots carefully surmised the gathering. Speaking slowly and distinctively, "Following Chief Joseph's narration will be an explanation of the Petition for the removal of President Andrew Jackson from the twenty dollar bill. When we up here in our heavenly retreat, can make contact with the earth people, our petition will be ready for circulation."

Sacajawea spoke out. "I suggest that we dramatize the riders galloping across the firmament collecting signatures to the musical accompaniment of the Wind Riders. In Native American culture, the flute holds a special place because of the power of its melodies to express love and healing. The best flute players were known as "wind riders" for their ability to harness the sound of air rushing through their instruments."

Among the gathering were former members of The Native Flute Ensemble. They communicated their pleasure and willingness by bringing forth their flutes and volunteering to give a demonstration. Enthusiastic approval was evident and the flute players, joined by ceremonial drummers performed a magnificent, melodious performance.

After the performance, the room echoed with sensory pleasure. Toni broke the silence saying, "This", as she held up the script, "is merely a formality. The true documentary will come from you and your inspiration." Her assistant broke a lengthy pause.

"Now we must go on with the third section of the film that is in question. Some members want to continue with the theme of "white removal" by advocating the removal of Theodore Roosevelt's visage from Mount Rushmore based on his immoral actions. Remember, President Theodore Roosevelt, in 1906, sent a letter of congratulations to the military commander who had ordered his troops to commit an atrocity against the Moros, inhabitants of an island in the Philippines, when the war was supposedly over. The village of six hundred unarmed men, women, and children were massacred."

"Why only Roosevelt's?" said Sanapia. "Those other three, Washington, Lincoln and Jefferson, I've studied their pasts and they were not too saintly."

"And remember", spoke out Chief Sioux, "That national monument is in the Black hills of South Dakota, the land of **our** initial homes."

Running Eagle in her buffalo shawl, breeches and moccasins, adamant as ever, faced Toni and Sacajawea and pronounced, "We already have discussed having the faces of Eugene Debs, Mother Jones, Frederick Douglas and Harriet Tubman carved on the other side of the mountain. I have spoken to Edmonia Lewis and she is very willing to accommodate us. So we can leave Roosevelt alone for a while."

Minnie Hollow Wood stood her grounds firmly as she added to the active debate, "We should include a poem from an Indian earthling, and I know just the one, Chrystos, a Native American (Menominee), lesbian born in 1946 and raised in San Francisco. She is a self-educated political activist and speaker, as well as an artist and writer. Her tireless momentum is directed at better understanding how issues of colonialism, genocide, class, and gender affect the lives of women and Native people and her poetry reflects this."

"That is a great suggestion. We start with a poem and end with a poem." Sarah Winniemucca, the outspoken critic of the treatment of Native Americans was all in favor of poetry that speaks to this condition.

"I'll submit three poems that I think are particularly appropriate and the director and her assistant, rather her self -appointed assistant, can make the final decision." Minnie Hollow Wood looked as regal as the beads in her braided hair as she made her statement.

"Let us see the poems you selected Minnie because I know you have done that prior to coming to the meeting." Toni with a deft nod of her head informed Sacajawea to go along with the decision.

"This one, *I Like To Think* is lengthy but all three are written with thoughtful conviction that is both sensual and scathing. I'd like to read the two short ones aloud so the community can hear for itself how well Chrystos blends ancient wisdom, humor, and heartfelt pain.

Minnie took center stage in the room and read:

The Rich
In their tennis whites lean over the roses
In the delicate sun
Discussing with the gardeners what to do
About the blight
As I iron their chaste sheets on both sides
The old fashion way
Crisp
They have purchased genuine coyote urine
From Maine
At a great expense
To keep the deer from nipping off the rosebuds
I imagine Coyote leaning over them
Saying with a sly chuckle
Listen
You give me some of that sweet money
& I'll piss all over you
Anytime

"I like old Coyote" said Chief Sitting Bull in approval of the reading. "What is the next one?"

"Very short and beautiful."

After a Long
Hard day working with no breaks
The sky welcomes me in a song
Of apricot lavender flamingo
One star burns beauty
Low over mountains etched
Copper & the moon
She blows me
A kiss Grinning silver

52

"What about the third one. Let's hear them all."

"Moving Robe, this is a documentary, not a poetry reading."

Chief Sitting Bull suggested that all three be read then a vote be taken.

I Like to Think
Of the Black miners in south africa
continually
I like to remember that they are always
Black
& always inspected thoroughly as they come
from the mines
bringing gold   silver   chrome   diamonds
for always white owners
I need to remember their wages
aligned with the price of diamonds & gold
jewelry
& so do you
I need to know
they plunder what is their own land
I like to think about the days they spend in total
darkness
about how long it is before they see their wives
& children
I like to remember the misery of death
under the gleam of necklaces   rings   cars
knives   spoons
I like to think of how much we have in common
stripping our lands for the master
I like to remember all the white owners
of Navaho rugs   Zuni jewelry   Lakota shirts
Pueblo pottery
Mohawk masks   Haida blankets   Pomo
baskets   Menominee copper
& the price of those things when whites sell
them
to each other after buying them from us for
dimes
or taking them

I like to remember some of our most beautiful
creations
dying in german & british museums
I like to remember the darkness of our world
where our lives are mere conveniences to their
acquisition
I need to remember that the Native design
towels
I want to buy at macy's   fill a white man's
pocket
I like to think of our relationship
boiled to a simple phrase
They take   We give
They take more
(*In honor of Ellen Kuzwayo*)

An appreciative and contemplative silence was not unlike an echo stemming from the final two lines. Toni and her assistant agreed to include all three poems in the documentary.

Malcolm and Sojourner were invited to stay and see the making of the film.

Sojourner declared that she appreciated being surprised when she watched movies and didn't want to know what happened before she saw what happened, so she and Malcolm would be moving on. Sister Toni said that she completely understood Sojourner's thoughts and to come back when she could be surprised.

Sojourner and Malcolm were still on the sacred grounds when Malcolm began their discussion starting with the fact that out of all 372 treaties that the United States government made with the Native Americans, not one, not a single one, was kept. Several minutes later, they were on Athletes Arena Avenue, the dwelling where the departed athletes lived.

Chapter Three Glossary & Endnotes

- *Eugene Debs (1855-1926):* United States Socialist leader, pacifist and labor organizer. He helped establish the Socialist Party of America and stood five times as Socialist candidate for U.S. Presidency from 1900 -1920. He was imprisoned from 1918 until 1921 for pacifist beliefs. He was a founding member of the International Labor Union and International workers of the World.

- *Harriet Tubman (1820-1913) aka "Black Moses":* She was born in Maryland, one of 11 children. Harriet escaped from the plantation and became a great fighter for freedom. Using an established underground route called the *"Underground Railroad"*, she made dangerous rescue trips to free her people. Along this route, friends and supporters provided safe hiding places, food and clothing. As a *"conductor"* on the *"Underground Railroad"* Harriet led more than 300 slaves to freedom and never lost a *"passenger."* She received many honors but spent her last years in poverty. When she finally received a monthly pension she used it to help establish a place for the aged and needy freedmen.

- *Ellen Kuzwayo (1914-2006):* South African born activist, teacher, social worker and author. Her autobiography "Call Me Woman" won South Africa's premier literary prize. She was the first Black South African to ever receive it. As an activist she challenged apartheid throughout her life. In 1977-8, she was imprisoned for five months at Johannesburg Fort. She was released without ever being charged. She was involved in the making of in two films and was the featured actress in "Awake from Mourning". In Soweto, where she lived in her later life, she was affectionately known as "Ma K". In 1946, she was secretary of the youth league of the ANC and involved in the Black Consciousness Movement. She was a key administrator in two women's self help organizations, Zamani Soweto Sisters and The Maggie Magaba Trust. She was oldest woman to serve in the new parliament of South Africa during Nelson Mandela's presidency.

CHAPTER IV

Athletes' Arena

The marble statue of the jockey sculpted with fine details was daunting and exquisite. It was the work of Mary Edmonia Lewis, the first Black American to receive recognition as a sculptor. Self taught she worked directly in marble and distinguished herself with many brilliant works. Her bust of the famed poet, Henry Wadsworth Longfellow can be seen in Harvard University's Widener Library. Here in the firmament she was still practicing her art. At present, she was working on sculpting four faces, a la Mount Rushmore, of Eugene Debs, Mother Jones, Harriet Tubman, and Frederick Douglass, for the entrance to the Native American quarters.

The statue was mounted on the right hand side of a large ebony arch that marked the entrance to Athletes Arena. It was a life size figure of Oliver Lewis, the first Black jockey - and the first *jockey* - to win the Kentucky Derby in the year 1875. Thirteen of the fourteen jockeys in the first race were Black. On the left hand side was a totem of balls, - ping-pong balls, golf balls, baseballs, volleyballs, footballs, soccer balls, basketballs, rugby balls, Lacrosse balls, field hockey balls, and a medicine ball.

The living quarters of the late athletes were arranged around a large room with decoration and design mirroring a combination of a living room and sports stadium. There were over sized, especially comfortable, and very colorful divans, chairs and recliners, lightweight exercise equipment and pool, billiard and card tables.

Life size photos of football firsts old fashion uniforms covering trim, muscular physiques lined one wall. On the north wall were black and white photos of the boxing greats, with their steroid- free bodies. Colorful pictures of athletic greats from all sports gave a curious blend of vitality and energy to the walls.

The plaque beside the photo of John Arthur Johnson known as Jack Johnson read:

"The first Black heavyweight champion"

Johnson became the "best boxer alive", but wanted a shot at the World Heavyweight Championship, held by Jim Jeffries. Jeffries response was, "I will not fight a Negro!" Jeffries retired from boxing but was asked to come out of retirement to become the **Great White Hope**. Johnson knocked out Jeffries in the 15th round. Boxing at this point became a symbol of triumph or failure of a whole people. Racism flourished in the history of sports and boxing was clearly defined as a Black and White contest for racial superiority.

Joe Louis known as the "Brown Bomber" was featured next to Johnson. Considered the greatest heavyweight of all time, Louis held the title of Heavy Weight World Champion for over 11 years. He was well known for his battles with Max Schmeling from Germany. Joe Louis represented the racial pride for all Black Americans. His first defeat by Schmeling left America stunned. In the re-match 1936, Louis knocked out Schmeling in the first round. The next day Blacks in Harlem, USA went around singing, "Hot ginger and dynamite, Joe Louis won the Fight."

A life-sized photo of Ernie Davis proudly holding the Heisman Trophy dominated the south wall. Davis was the first Black to win the Heisman Trophy—college football's highest honor. He won the trophy in 1961. Sadly, in 1963 at age 23, Ernie Davis died of leukemia never having played in the National Football League (NFL). Other football greats along with basketball players filled the south wall.

In the center of the hall, a beverage dispenser advertised a variety of sports drinks claiming to be thirst quenching as well as containing electrolytes, energy building blocks and proteins. There was a food bar with healthy snacks specializing in peanuts of all descriptions - salted, roasted, unsalted, honey coated, crystallized, cashews, and pistachios. The Southern boys preferred their traditional plain old goobers.

A hotdog stand was installed especially for Babe Ruth who still loved his hot dogs. He was frequently seen at the stand with his rotund physique and spindly legs, wearing either a Red Sox or Yankee jersey. Nick- named the Sultan of Swat and the Bambino, Ruth played for the Boston Red Socks for six years before his contract was sold to the Yankees.

This morning Babe Herman Ruth was standing in front of the refreshment stand deciding whether to start his day with the 'full doggie' that meant a hot dog with sauerkraut, onions, mustard, ketchup, and relish or the 'regular doggie' with just mustard and relish.

Josh Gibson came up behind him saying, "Bambino Babe, go on and order the 'full doggie', during your hey -day diet never interfered with your pitching or batting so why the hesitation."

Josh Gibson widely known as the Black Babe Ruth was popular, brash, and fun loving as a youth and a favorite among the athletes in the arena.

"So now you're giving advice about eating habits. Listen you whippersnapper, you were still in diapers when I was playing in the big time leagues, the major leagues," was Babe's good natured response."

"Yeah, but the only reason I never played in the major leagues was because of the color barriers. Babe, the public keeps trying to compare our batting records, our home run productivity. You hit your 714 home runs before the major leagues became integrated and during my 17-year career, I hit as many as 962 homers, but they were against semi-pro competition. Even though many of the Black semi-pro players were as good as and better than the white players in the major leagues, as far as records go, I never played against major league competition."

"I know all about that, man, and racism in sports still stinks to high heavens."

"Be careful what you saying, man, don't nothing stink up here, remember where we are", said the jokester Josh.

"Yeah, but there's no telling what your records would have been Josh, if you hadn't died at such a young age 35 with that brain tumor."

Josh sill a solid six one and 215 pounds, and still strong as an ox, recounted, "During the last years of my life, I just lost my mind, so to say. There was the death of my wife giving birth to twins, that my twin sister willingly cared for, plus my heavy drinking pot smoking and headaches associated with the brain tumor diagnosis, add to that the disappointment in knowing that you are good enough for the major leagues and based on color you excluded, well ain't that enough to drive a man insane!"
Babe, having decided on two 'full doggies' sat down on a barstool rested his elbows on the counter. He devoured one third of the full doggie in one bite and started talking.

Josh quickly said, "Babe, slow down, nobody's going to take away your food and even though I had a working class background I was taught not to speak with a mouth full of food", grinned Gibson.

Babe Herman Ruth smiled but kept on chewing. He wiped a bit of mustard from his mouth, swallowed, and then spoke out. "Let me tell you about our similarities. We both were natural hitters, teenage sensations when it came to hitting that little ball. And we both came from working class families. You had prodigious power, how do you like that word, - pro- di-gi –ous. Man, you had pure unadulterated, non-steroid power. Legends about how far and how many homeruns you hit are still being bantered around. Stories like the time kids perched in a tree outside of the stadium, 500 feet from home plate, had to scatter as the ball you hit came zooming by."

Josh laughed. "Yeah, there are some ticklish stories out there, but we sure did have some good times. Despite the Jim Crow laws, poor pay and the truly terrible traveling and housing conditions, -

sleeping on the buses many times, - despite all that, we provided years of fun, recreational pleasures and enjoyment for Black and White spectators. We players led a sportin' life especially on those barnstorming tours, show- boating and clowning on the field, carousing and drinking off the field and women and kids worshipping and adoring us"

After several swallows of root beer Ruth added, "You guys in the Retreat have uniforms from five or six different teams because of the frequent buying and selling of teams as well as players. On the other hand, I was with the Red Sox for six years until my contract was sold to the Yankees in 1920. The Red Sox fans never forgave the owner for selling me."

"Yep, that was the start of the, 'Curse of the Bambino'. Since the Red Sox failed to win a world series for more than eight decades afterward, the fans declared that there was a spell, a curse on them for selling you."
Josh flexed the muscles of his massive forearms and extended his arms forward, proclaiming, "Babe Ruth, you are one of the greatest sports heroes in American culture. You are recognized as one of the most gifted and popular players in the history of baseball. Now look at me, Josh Gibson, recognized by many as the greatest home-run hitter of all times. What's the big difference between us? History knows and hears about Babe Ruth, even got a candy bar named after you. They should have a candy bar made of dark chocolate and pecans with a stripe of molasses and call it "The Josh Gibson." As for me, those familiar with the Negro Baseball League know of me, but very few others. So from now on, earth folks, when you mention Babe Ruth, remember and say out loud that Josh Gibson also was a King of Swat."

Babe having finished his snack turned toward Josh and said, "Can't argue with that, Gibson." Hearing a commotion coming from the Celestial Gazer area, Babe said, "Lets' see what the old baseball geezers are up to today." And they headed to the gazers.

Several Celestial Gazers were situated on the outskirts of the room and the athletes spent hours checking out the sporting activities of the earthlings. This morning all five Celestial Gazers were surrounded by animated on lookers and the customary good humored, light-hearted trash talking, joking, shucking and jiving and telling tales that were elaborated, exaggerated and glamorized was in high gear.

At present all the attention of the athletes was on the Gazer, beamed in on stations that were following the Barry Bonds saga. Bonds, who was accused of using steroids and or other performance enhancing substances was rapidly gaining on Hank Aaron's record of 755 career home runs.

"Hank Aaron is a first class, man of dignity who hit 755 legitimate National League career homeruns", spoke up the quiet easy going Walter "Buck" Leonard who when paired with Josh Gibson led their team to nine consecutive Negro League championships. "Bonds will undoubtedly surpass him but I don't know if I can consider Bonds' homeruns as being legitimate as Hank's"

"Babe Ruth hit 714 home runs, wasn't it? It took 52 years for anyone to top that mark and Hank Aaron did that but records are made to be broken and along comes Barry", chimed in James 'Cool Papa' Bell. "But I'm willing to let the current crop of baseball big wigs settle the situation because we don't have a say in the matter anyway."

The truly old timers were well seasoned with scars of their trade. The old breaks and fractures, cuts and bruises, the limping and gingerly gaits did not hide their pride and enduring passion for the game as they moved around the stadium/living room. They usually wore their old styled uniforms, knickers, knee socks, sneakers or sandals (no spikes) and short sleeve shirts with the names of their teams.
A host of players from the Negro National League that started around 1920 and folded in 1948, included Rube Foster, Josh Gibson, Buck Leonard, Cool Papa Bell, Smokey Joe Williams and

Buck O'Neil. They represented a colorful collection of trash talkers and were divided on the subject of Barry Bond's use of illegal substances.

"What I want to know", said Andrew "Rube" Foster, "is whether or not his home runs were enhanced?" Rube Foster, a big Texan, received his nickname Rube, after a victory over the great white star, Rube Waddell, in an exhibition game in 1902. Foster was a smart, dominant pitcher and had brilliant managerial skills. He established the best Black baseball teams and organized the Negro National League. Unfortunately, he suffered a nervous breakdown and in 1925 entered a state asylum for the mentally impaired. He died there in 1930.

James "Cool Papa" Bell still maintaining his sleek 5' 11" build was holding court. Seated on the edge of an armchair he pointed his index finger at the group and pronouncing every word slowly and deliberately said, "It's a question of what they calling drugs. Now we didn't have no steroid injections in our days but we sure had other kinds of stimulation. How about them good ole plugs of chewing tobaccy and snuff, not to mention shots of strong likka, you know like white lightening and red eye whiskey. You could say they enhanced our performances."

"Papa Bell, how in the world you going to compare liquor and tobacco to steroids?" questioned Rube Foster.

"You don't know what all went into that likka. Hoochy-choochy folks brewed some of it and who knows what was in that tobacco as we rolled our own. Mary Jane was popular with a lot of fellers, you know", continued Cool Papa Bell.
There were two reigning opinions; if Bonds is cleared of the accusations, there should be no question about his record setting being legitimate. On the other hand if he is guilty of using drugs, his record should stand with the indication that he had some outside help.

Toni Stone and Connie Morgan and Mamie Peanut Johnson were the only women to have played in the Negro Leagues, and their baseball lives were intertwined.

Mamie Peanut Johnson was in her seventies and still on earth. In 1952, she was denied admission to the white Female Baseball League due to laws of segregation. She was a pitcher with the Indianapolis Clowns from 1953 to 1955.

This morning Toni Stone, (*born Marcenia Lyle Alberga*), the first woman to play in the Negro Leagues, and Connie Morgan were animatedly involved in the conversation around the Gazer.

Toni raised her voice over the male tones. "Do you guys know that in 1953, the owner of the Indianapolis Clowns signed me to play second base, a position vacated by Hank Aaron when he was signed by the Boston Braves? Yeah, it's the same Hank Aaron that y'all talking about. Do you guys remember that? I wasn't allowed, 'no Blacks allowed', to play in the "white only" all American Girls Baseball League, but I was good enough to replace Hank Aaron."

"All three of you were good enough to play in any all Women's Leagues and you all sure should have been starring in that movie, "A League of Their Own", piped in Rube Foster.

Toni continued, "After a year I played with the famed Kansas City Monarchs. When I left the Clowns, who did they hire to replace me at second base?"

Connie gracefully leaped out of her chair, performed an outrageous bow from the waist and with her right hand sweeping widely announced, " None other than yours truly, Constance "Connie" Enola Morgan, the 19 year old, right handed second baseman, -no, second basewoman, - and for five seasons maintained a 368 batting average."

Cool Papa Bell said, "I know my baseball history, and the same time you, Connie, replaced Toni, a female pitcher named Mamie

"Peanuts" Johnson was signed. But I gotta say your 368 batting average was when you were playing on women's teams."

Toni came to the defense of her friend, "Mr. Cool, we know of your blazing speed on the bases, stealing two bases on a single pitch, a switch hitter and pitcher as well, but that doesn't give you license to be dishin' Connie's more than outstanding batting record."

Connie and Toni arrived in Revolutionary's Retreat in respectively in October and November of 1996. They too liked to wear their old uniforms but they also liked to show off the latest in sports fashion for women in 2007. So today, Connie was wearing coral Baby French capris and a matching zip front jacket. Toni sported a yellow cotton pique knit top and bright green stretch pants with side-scoop pockets.

From her red-leathered covered recliner Connie sat up and proclaimed, "The past is the past, Papa Bell and our records stand untainted. We're talking now about the present and I say that if the men need extra help to perform, then NO, they have no business competing for records that other players established without using illegal substances. They need to enter a special contest only for steroids and human growth hormone users."

Toni agreed and commented, "That's right Connie. Can't the men measure up on their own merits?"

From across the room, peering into a second Gazer were Althea Gibson and Babe Didrikson Zaharias. Babe shouted, "Of course they can't. That's why they have Viagra." A burst of hearty laughter came from the women. "And you notice when discussing men's sexual problems they don't say they have a 'sick dick' or' wimpy weenie', no they give it a sophisticated name like, *erectile dysfunction*. Now when it comes to women, they call them 'frigid'."

"All I got to say is that it's a good thing they didn't test testosterone levels in female athletes back in the earlier days", retorted Josh Gibson.

"Well I'm glad that's all you got to say because now you can shut up. Just chill." This came from Althea who from her Harlem days could street talk with the best of them.

At this moment Flora (Flo) Hyman her thin six foot five body, clad in a light blue warm up suit entered the room. She was during her brief lifetime of thirty years the best players in the history of women's volleyball. She was known for her awesome spiking abilities as well as for her dignity and spirit. She had suffered from a congenital disorder, Marfan's syndrome that affects tall, thin people in particular.

Rube Foster affectionately greeted her, "Flo, you're a deeply committed athlete with good sense. Tell these folks what you think about Barry Bonds"

"I'll let the earthlings settle that controversy," she said with a smile. "What I can say is that in due time I think that he definitely deserves to be in the Negro Leagues Baseball Museum in Kansas City, Missouri."

"I appreciate baseball museums but make sure they don't exhibit some stinking socks, smelly jock straps and mud stained pants when they show case Bonds. And maybe a sample of his 'enhancement drugs' should be included."

"Connie Morgan", countered Josh Gibson, "You dishin' our museum. You need to beam in on the Negro Leagues Baseball Museum so you can see how important that museum is. It's important for young people for all people to know our history so they can see how successful we were despite the consistent prejudices and discrimination practiced in sports throughout the USA."

Flo Hyman nodded in agreement, as she went to join Althea and Babe at their Celestial Gazer. The baseball enthusiast continued their banter as they kept watch on Barry Bonds' performance.

Althea Gibson and Babe Zaharias, cut buddies in Revolutionary's Retreat, frequented the tennis and golf strata channels. Flo Hyman joined them on the air cushioned chamois covered arm-chairs arranged in a semi circle around the Gazer. They were commenting on the large number of Russian women in tennis today and particularly in contrast to the meager number of American women, and particularly Black women.

Althea Gibson the first Black to win a major tennis title won the French Open Women's singles title on May 29, 1956. On July 6, 1957, she became the first Black to win a Wimbledon championship and on September 8, 1957, she became the first black to win a national championship by defeating Louise Brough at Forest Hills, New York. That year she was ranked the top female tennis player in the world.

Flo said, "Althea you did it all way back in the '50's. Why the present shortage of Black women tennis players? There were Zina Garrison and Lori McNeil. Now all I hear about are the Williams sisters, Venus and Serena."

Babe Zaharias who was always on top of women's sports exclaimed, "Flo, most people never even heard of the Peters sisters, Margaret and Matilda Roumania, nick named "Pete" and "Repeat" Long before the William sisters became tennis celebrities the Peters sisters were nationally known tennis stars. From the late 1930's into the early '50's, those two Tuskegee University graduates won a record 14, yes 14, American Tennis Association doubles championships. Margaret died at age 90, and Matilda Roumania who died in May 2003, at the age of 85, held the distinction of being the only African American woman known to have beaten Althea," Babe continued with a wink at Althea.

"She did but I was a youngster then and they passed the torch to me. They faced and fought the racial barriers and prejudices just as I did and you had better believe me, the Williams sisters are facing it today. It's ironic that the United States Tennis Association honored the Peters sisters with an achievement award in 2003 during the Federation Cup finals in D.C. And this was the same organization they could not be a part of during their playing days, simply because of their skin color. The Peters sisters were tennis legends in their days. Arthur Ashe and I were legends in our days, and today, well-- the state of affairs of Black athletes/celebrities is too complicated for a one-liner.

Flo added, "Babe, I didn't know about the Peters sisters until I met them up here but I certainly know that it takes tremendous dedication and hard work to become a champion. So despite criticisms that I hear about the William sisters and their father, they are still champions so they must be doing something right."

"Doing some things right doesn't mean that at the same time you could be doing things that are not right. There are errors of omission and errors of commission," said Babe.

Althea interjected, "Flo, this much I know. I was intimidating with one of the most powerful serves, pinpoint volleys and a huge overhead smash. Venus Williams has these same qualities and talents and with specialized coaching in her service and net play, girl, there's no one on the circuit at this time that could beat her with any consistency. She's tall like I was and when you come up to the net with that wide wing span, looking like some kind of bat out of hell, your opponent is intimidated and in trying to pass you, and unless she's really sharp the shot misses the court."

"There are a lot of fathers out their coaching their daughters and they themselves need to go to Nick Bolleteri's tennis school to learn some manners and etiquette. Daddy doesn't always know best", wise cracked Babe. "But I think Serena is awesome. That young lady has the will power, muscle power and a fighting spirit of Queen Nzinga from Angola, Shaka Zulu and Hercules all rolled into one. Those two sisters deserve all the credit in the world. They were young, and unfamiliar and not accustomed to the chicanery, back stabbing, racism, elitism, and cut throat competition in the sport world, they survived and succeeded."

68

"In answer to your question Flo, as to why the shortage of Black women tennis players and golfers too for that matter", answered Althea. "To begin with it takes money and time and commitment and dedication. You need money for coaches, travel expenses, equipment, clothing, tuition for attending a tennis academy and these are basic. I didn't have money but I did have a few individuals who noticed my talents, took an interest in me, and sponsored me. As I see the huge salaries today's Black athletes make, if each one would sponsor one male and one female youngster, provide them with the guidance and monetary needs, the shortage would soon be over."

The trio, Babe, Flo and Althea turned their attention to the golf strata channel.

Babe Didrikson Zaharias as an athlete was in a class of her own. Without doubt, she should be recognized as the greatest athlete, male or female, known to the world. She excelled in running, swimming, diving, high jump, baseball, and basketball in addition to being adept with the javelin and hurdles. During the 1932 Olympic Games at Los Angeles, she won the javelin throw and 80-meter hurdles.

Watching the golf channel prompted Althea to talk about her brief and rather unsuccessful golfing career. "In 1958 I retired from tennis competition and broke another color barrier by becoming the first African American woman to compete on the LPGA circuit. It's not easy on that circuit. In a seven-year span, I won ONE tournament. On the other hand, look at Babe. At age 21 she took up golf and beginning in 1940, captured the Western and Texas Open Championships. By the end of 1950, she had won every available golf title. The Russian players are dominating tennis in numbers and performance. In golf, the Korean players are dominating in numbers and winning tournaments. And don't forget Michele Wie. What's the story behind that Babe?"

"Well, like you were saying about tennis there's a need for sponsorships and encouragement. Those Korean girls, for them golf is a ticket to a lucrative future. It offers money, travel, and fame. As for Michelle Wie, she needs to take a one-year break from competition and live out her adolescence, then begin again. Since turning pro in 2005, to date, 2007, she has no professional wins. The golfing world put unreasonable expectations on her. At age 12, she was the youngest player to qualify for an LPGA event. At ages 12, 13 and 14 she was flying high on her kinetic energy and talent. Turning pro in 2005, she entered events beyond her mental and emotional capabilities as well as physical development and started a fast free fall downwards. You can't speed up maturation. Her parents, the public, the entire golfing world should stop trying to manufacture a sport celebrity at the personal expense of the individual.

Now on another topic the high tech golf clubs that they produce today makes it a handicap not to own them. When I was playing with my hickory shaft woods, I drove 240 yards easily. If I could return to earth I would beat them all", said Babe reverting to her teen-age style of talking out the side of her mouth.
"You also once pitched for the St. Louis Cardinals in an exhibition game and toured the United States giving billiard exhibitions. And why were you nicknamed after Babe Ruth? After hitting five homeruns in a baseball game—you are in a class by yourself."

Willye White calling to her across the room interrupted Althea's comments. Willye, Gertrude Ederle, Susan Butcher, and Jesse Owens were crowded around a Gazer checking out worldwide sports. Willye White a recent arrival at the Arena was born in Mississippi in 1939 and was the first American track and field athlete to compete in five Olympics, from 1956 to 1972. The long jump was her specialty and she won two Olympic silver medals and nine consecutive U.S. outdoor championships. In 1960, she moved to Chicago and was a government health administrator and director of recreational services.

"Althea, you all check out strata channel number twelve. The star quarterback for the Atlanta Falcons, Michael Vick, is involved in the business of dog fighting and Susan Butcher is about to have a natural fit."

70

Susan Butcher was a four-time winner of the Iditarod Sled Dog Race. Dog sled racing is an extremely physically demanding sport requiring the mushers and their teams to battle the elements on a 1,000-plus mile trek between Anchorage and Nome, Alaska. It honors the history of dog mushing. To Butcher any thought of mistreatment of dogs hit her nerve centers hard.

"This is just one case that's being publicized and investigated because a popular personality is involved. Dog fighting is a wide spread cruel, loathsome practice. I won't honor it by calling it a sport or entertainment. For a country that is so dog loving I don't see why there aren't tougher laws. No, not laws, simply abolish the practice then there would be no need for laws", lamented Susan.

Jesse Owens, Willye, Gertrude and Susan Butcher shifted their attention from the Gazer and became engrossed in the conversation.

"Do you know what's one of the most popular tourist attractions in Central Park in NYC?" asked Susan Butcher. Before anyone could answer she continued, "The statue of Balto, the lead dog on the last relay team. It is dedicated to all the dogs involved in the serum run."
"The serum run? What are you talking about Susan?" asked Gertrude Ederle who had won one gold and two bronze medals in swimming at the 1924 Olympics in Paris, France.

Before Susan could answer, a new voice was heard. "Hello fellow athletes. What's causing all this electricity I feel in the air?" The first woman ever to earn three gold medals in track occurred in Rome Italy in 1960, the 1960 "Athlete of the Year" entered and joined the group around the celestial gazer.

"'Wilma, Wilma 'Rudy' Rudolph, where you been lately? From the looks of that classy warm-up suit looks like you been shopping in high fashion boutiques."

"Nothing of the sort, Willye, actually it's one of Venus' Williams new line of clothing and listen to this, each item, each piece of clothing costs only twenty dollars or less. Now isn't that admirable and worthy of compliments?"

"That's a great move on Venus' part. Not like some star athletes endorsing basketball, shoes that sell for one hundred and two hundred dollars and then you have youngsters fighting, robbing, and even killing one another just to get a pair of those shoes. I know that because I departed the earth below in February of 2007. And in most cases, slave labor and materials that actually costs a few dollars produced the shoes. We need more athletes to show a social and economic consciousness.

We were in the midst of discussing Michael Vick's involvement in dog fighting and that electricity you felt came from our collective outrage," commented Willye.

"I want to hear more about the serum run. Was it a race?"

"Wilma, indeed it was and what a race." The group as one body leaned forward, eyes riveted on Susan Butcher as the vibrations and tone of her voice escalated and descended alternately.

"It was the year 1925 in Nome, Alaska when an outbreak of diphtheria happened. Nome lies two degrees south of the Arctic Circle and from November to July is icebound and at that time inaccessible by steamship. The only link to the outside world during the winter was the Iditarod Trail, which ran 938 miles from the port in the south, across several mountain ranges and the vast Alaska Interior before reaching Nome. Later bush pilots were used for mail and needed supplies, but in 1925, it was the dog sled.
On January 22, 1925, a radio telegram sent to Washington, D.C. stated that a major epidemic of diphtheria was almost inevitable and there was an urgent need for one million units of diphtheria anti-toxin. A previous influenza epidemic across the Seward Peninsula in 1918 and 1919 wiped out about 50% of the native population of Nome. In response to the telegram, a proposal to fly

the antitoxin by aircraft was not feasible since the only planes operating in Alaska in 1925 were three World War I vintages that were unsuited and unreliable in cold weather. The Board of Health voted unanimously for the dog sled relay."

"Now wait a minute, Susan", said Jesse looking a bit bewildered. "Let me get this straight. This city, town, village, whatever it is, Nome, is in danger of having a major diphtheria epidemic and they are isolated from the outside world. Now this serum, antitoxin has to get to the people in a real hurry and the best way is dog sleds?"

"The *only way*, Jesse."

"Well where did they get the serum from and how far did you say they had to travel to get to Nome, Alaska?" Gertrude Ederle too was looking somewhat mystified as she ran her fingers through her bob hair.

"The public health services were able to located 300,000 units from hospitals as an initial shipment and it would go by ship to Seattle, then transported to Alaska. The mail route ran from Nenana to Nome and the best mail carriers were used in relay teams to transport the serum. Mail carriers were highly esteemed in the territory and were the best dog punchers in Alaska. Most relay drivers across the interior were native Athabaskans, direct descendants of the original dog mushers. On January 27, the first musher in the relay was "Wild Bill" Shannon, who was handed the 20-pound package at the train station in Nenana. The relay teams of dogs and mushers saved the small city of Nome and the surrounding communities from an incipient epidemic."

"This statue in Central Park is dedicated to the dogs? What about the men called mushers?" Jesse was still a bit perplexed

"The 1925 serum run to Nome is also known as the "Great Race of Mercy." 20 mushers and about 150 sled dogs relayed diphtheria antitoxin 674 miles by dog sled across the U.S. territory of Alaska in a record- breaking five and a half days. Compare that time to this: mail transported 420 miles by train from the ice free port of Seward to Nenana, and then transported the 674 miles from Nenana to Nome by dog sled normally took 25 days!"

The listeners along with Jesse, eager for more details plied Susan with queries, "How many dogs to a team? When did they rest? How cold was it?"

Nodding vigorously and rocking slightly back and forth Susan spoke like a griots. "The first musher, Shannon, had a team of nine inexperienced dogs led by Blackie in temperatures minus 50 degrees Fahrenheit. Shannon jogged beside the sled to keep warm and still developed hypothermia. He reached Minto, with parts of his face black from frostbite. After warming the serum by the fire and resting for four hours, he dropped off three dogs and left with the remaining six. The second relay team was led by musher Kallands with the temperature minus 56 degrees F, and when he arrived at the next station he had to have hot water over his hands to get them off the sled's handle bars."

"What? How could they endure all of that?"

"That's why they and their dogs are heroes. Not only did the drivers suffer. One musher forgot to protect the groins of his two shorthaired mixed breed lead dogs with rabbit skin, when they passed through ice fog and a river had broken through and surged over the ice, and both dogs collapsed with frostbite. On another occasion the conditions were so drastic with visibility zero, the lead dog used his senses to follow the trail that was covered with ice and snow. The longest and most hazard leg of the trip was covered by musher Seppala and his lead dog Togo. They made a round trip that almost doubled the distance of any other team. Balto was the lead dog on the Rohn's team that reached Nome February 3, 1925. Many considered Togo to be the real hero in the race.

In October 1926, Seppala took Togo and his team on a tour from Seattle to California. In New England Seppala's team of Siberian huskies ran in many races, easily defeating the local Chinooks. Seppala sold most of his team to a kennel in Poland Springs, Maine, and most huskies can trace their descent from one of these dogs."

"So, Balto has a statue in NYC. What about Togo?" asked Wilma. "Seppala visited Togo, who was in retirement until he was euthanized on December 5, 1929. After his death, Seppala had Togo preserved and mounted, and today the dog is on display in a glass case at the Iditarod museum in Wasilla, Alaska."

"Wow!" said Willye. "Those men were surely devoted to their dogs, particularly Seppala. And here we have men engaging dogs in a brutal carnage calling it a sport. Thanks for that story Susan. I have a deeper understanding of your feeling for dogs."

Susan smiled in appreciation from the response of her friends.

"Dog fighting, cock fighting, Grey hound dog racing, that fox chase they have in England, all need to be outlawed. I imagine that for some folks it provides entertainment and enjoyment but to my way of thinking you got to have a mean mind to enjoy such things", commented Jesse.

"It's so peaceful and free feeling up here in the firmament that at times you tend to forget the past and the injustices that we and others suffered. Now Jesse, as outstanding an athlete as you were, as successful as you were and all the glory you brought to the United States, man you was mistreated beyond words," said Willye White.

"As a white woman, I know the hardships of sexist discrimination, but it shatters me when I hear all that you went through", spoke out Susan.

"Jesse's experiences need to be heard by all these young athletes of today some who are rich as Croesus yet they don't know how to clean their own behinds without getting shit all over themselves.

They don't remember that as late as 1933, we were still struggling with desegregation. In college, Jesse had to live off campus with other African American athletes. When traveling with the team he had to eat at "blacks only" restaurants and sleep in "blacks only" hotels. On occasions when the Black athletes were allowed to stay in the hotels, they had to use the back door and stairs instead of the elevator. "

Willye was vehement as she continued, "In 1936 at the Olympics in Germany, known as the Hitler Olympics when Hitler was proving the superiority of the Aryan race, Jesse you were the first American in the history of Olympic Track and Field to win four gold medals in a single Olympics! And did you get any endorsements? Of course not! Blacks were not offered endorsements then. And today, these young Black stars get millions for endorsing over priced sneakers, and all sorts of non-nutritious drinks and snacks."

"I think the worst the most un-believable signature of a country in terms of treatment of a man of Jesse's stature was the fact that in order to provide for his family he had to take on a role of a "runner-for-hire" racing against anything from people, to horses, to motorcycles! The Negro Baseball League often hired him to race against thoroughbred horses in an exhibition before every game. Of course at that time these were good will actions to help him financially but such a statement for justice", continued Susan Butcher.

Jesse spoke for himself, "There's no doubt, I underwent many trials, tribulations and successes but beneath it all, I remained James Cleveland Owens, a family man of God willing to work for my achievements no matter how hard the road. And remember, after all the hardships I emerged victorious. In 1976, I was awarded the highest honor a United States civilian can get. President Ford awarded me the Medal of Freedom."

"Medal of Freedom! Was that supposed to mean that you were free from bigotry, racism, and segregation?", blurted Willye.

76

"No, but it shows that no obstacles were greater than my God given abilities. And my family and I are proud of that. In addition, I was posthumously awarded the Congressional Gold Medal in 1990 by President George H.W. Bush in recognition of my triumphs."

"Those presidents sure know how to honor people. Too bad they can't do more to end discrimination and bigotry. Jesse you sure are a humble, faithful, and forgiving man."

Sojourner and Malcolm were in front of Athlete's Arena, walking at a calm, leisurely pace. Hearing the animation and commotion of the athlete's voices, they decided to continue their stroll without interrupting the loquacious elocutionists.

Chapter Four Glossary & Endnotes

- *Barry Bonds*: Born July 1964 in Riverside, California. Major League baseball player with the San Francisco Giants (2007.) As of July 27, 2007, Bonds is one homerun away from tying Hank Aaron's record of 755 career homeruns. His most significant records include the single season major league records for home runs (73) being the all time leader in walks (2517) and intentional walks (675) and having received seven MVP awards. (*Most Valuable Player*). Since 2003, Bonds has been a key figure in the BALCO scandal and is accused of using steroids and other performance enhancing substances. He is under investigation for perjury by a federal grand jury.

- *"A League of Their Own"*: A 1992 comedy-drama film that tells a fictionalized account of the real-life All-American Girls Professional Baseball League (*AABPGL*). Film stars included Geena Davis, Tom Hanks, Madonna, Lori Petty and Rosie O'Donnell. No Black women ball players were in the cast.

- *"Mary Jane"*: Cannabis sativa aka marijuana.

- *Hoochy-choochy*: A man or woman who practices voodoo.

- *Gertrude Ederle (1905-2003)*: An American competitive swimmer who in 1926 became the first woman to swim the English Channel. At the 1924 summer Olympics, she won a gold medal as a part of the 400-meter freestyle relay team and two bronze medals. Her famous cross-channel swim began in France, August 1926. 14 hours and 30 minutes later she came ashore at England. Her record stood until Florence Chadick swam the channel in 1950 in 13 hours and 20 minutes.

Chapter V

Caribbean Corners

Caribbean Corners was the domain of revolutionaries whose navel strings were buried in the backyards of their Caribbean islands. Flags for each of the islands, in many brilliant colors - the green, gold, black of Jamaica; red and blue of Haiti –after throwing out the white color when they gained their freedom - yellow, red and green of Grenada; the black, blue and yellow of the Bahamas -fluttered and danced over the archway of the entrance. The archway was formed by two ultra-bright orange flamboyant trees planted on opposite sides. The trees had reached out, touched one another, and become seductively entwined.

Side by side, in syncopated steps, leisurely strolling down the pathway bordered with various sized delicate, rosy, pink conch shells, were Maurice Bishop and Kwame Ture. This morning, like all other mornings, these tall, handsome men were eager to reach the courtyard that was the main gathering spot for West Indian style breakfasts and outrageous kidding. Bishop had an ongoing joking relationship with Nanny the Maroon, and Kwame was ever ready to analyze, dissect, and puncture the theories and concepts that anyone presented.

· "Kwame, today I am ready for Nanny's barbs. That woman is so wise and witty that if you're not constantly on the alert she can disarm you in a squinet which is less than a minute."

"We'll see", laughed Kwame as they entered the courtyard.

There were plenty, plenty coconut trees that provided both shade and nuts. Other fruit bearing trees - bananas, tamarind, pomegranate, genip, sour sop, sorrel, golden apples, mesple, papaya, oranges, limes, avocados and mangoes "knockin' dog", produced an abundance of luscious scented, fresh, off the vines nutriments. The familiar sounds of Bob Marley's recordings were confined to the community grounds. This morning the reggae sound of the all time favorite, *"Three Little Birds"*, provided background music.

Under palm trees, squatting on their haunches, were rebel leaders Nanny, the Jamaican Maroon, Amy Jacques also Jamaican, and three young Crucian women, Queen Mary or Captain Thomas, Axelline Solomon called Queen Agnes and Queen Matilda McBean known as Bottom Belly. A fourth young Crucian woman, Queen Susanna Abramson hadn't arrived as yet.

Nearby, C. L. R. James, an Anglo-Trinidadian, journalist, social theorist, and playwright, and Walter Rodney, a Guyanese historian of international fame, were lounging on sun deck chairs in the shade of a tamarind tree.

The lively group was telling stories about their struggles for emancipation, freedom, justice, equality and an overall end to oppressions. Their animated conversations were abiding by absolutely no rules of order. Laughter, interruptions, contradictions, sober moments, over talking and interjections were the unwritten guidelines for the discussions.

As Kwame and Maurice entered the grounds, Nanny called out, "Good morning gentlemen from the late arrival brigade. I'll wager that the reason you are so late is because you spent so much time selecting those dashing, colorful, embroidered dashikis."

"Nanny, this morning after I have consumed my late breakfast, I am going to return to yesterday's unfinished discussion about your well undocumented, magical, super human exploits in the forests and hills of Jamaica," baited Maurice giving Kwame a knowing smile.

Queen Mary washed down her dumb bread with coconut water, rose from her squatting position and accompanied the latecomers to the beverages and victuals. Ginger beer and bush teas dominated the beverage table. The breakfast table was crowded with Johnnycakes, dumb bread, salt fish, gundy, boiled eggs, cassava bread, guava berry jam, red grout, guava, pineapple and mango tarts and a variety of fruits. The men helped themselves to generous portions and settled down next to Walter and C. L. R. James.

Walter Rodney, slight of stature, with tailor fit, Atlantic blue, lightweight trousers and a classic seersucker, red glen plaid short-sleeved shirt with button down collar, went to the fruit bowl searching for a sugar apple with the exact ripeness for his taste. Fingering an apple he commented amusingly, "Brother Prime Minister Bishop, are you planning to re-engage Nanny in still another discussion on the sophistication of your regime compared to her jungle activities?"
"Not today Walter, I am not going to spend one iota of time describing and explaining the invasion of, my tiny spice island, Grenada. That story is very well documented, with detailed factual historical information with precise descriptions and explanations of the entire event. It's all there in a pamphlet titled, *"GRENADA: This Invasion Was Not Televised."* I'm going to advise Nanny to read it before any further discussion." (*See Glossary & Endnotes*)

Kwame quickly interjected, "Walter, you had better not let Nanny hear you talking about 'jungle activities'- sounds too much like 'jungle bunnies'."

"Too late," said Bishop, as Nanny with movements reminiscent of her guerilla days, moved from the palm trees to the circle of men.

"*You*, Dr. Walter Rodney, historian, and leader of the Working People's Alliance in Guyana, and *you*, Prime Minister Bishop, neither one of you had the good sense to escape your enemies during your modern times. You had all kinds of sophisticated political theories and advanced technology, plus bodyguards and look what happened to the both of you. Brothers, you underestimated the treachery and callousness of your opposition."

'Oh, no, listen to Nanny signifying and sounding on my comrades' mused Kwame. She's referring to the fact that Walter Rodney was killed by a bomb that exploded in the car he was riding in and after years of delays and inquiries, the government decreed that his death was due to 'mis-adventure' not assassination. The truth of the matter was that Rodney was killed because of his opposition to the corrupt ruling Guyanese government. And as for Bishop, she always accused him of not knowing who to trust and who to fear.'

Lithe and agile, with strong, captivating Ashanti features, the Jamaican rebel woman prior to continuing her remarks gave a slight movement of her head in the direction of the other women. Casually, Amy Jacques, Queens Mary, Agnes and Matilda formed a semi-circle behind Nanny.

Bishop cajoled, "Now Nanny, you are no longer doing battle in the Jamaican mountains, so you don't need this modified sphincter movement."

Nanny a leader of the Maroons, a guerilla woman, was the most outstanding civic and military leader in the history of Black freedom movements and the first national heroine of Jamaica. The island of Jamaica was an excellent guerrilla warfare country with its dense forests, deep mountain hollows, rivers, and creeks. Many slaves escaped from the British owned plantations and led the lives of bush-rebels. These men and women refused to be enslaved and created a free world for themselves in the bush and were called Maroons They established free villages, led a healthy outdoor life and were rid of plantation labor and punishment.

Nanny continued, "I fought many fierce battles in the Blue Mountains of Jamaica and you may call it 'jungle activities', but let me tell you my fighting strategies of yesteryear are considered today as strategies of a genius as I directed guerilla campaigns using science and," at this point Nanny uttered a devilish, cackling, "heh, heh, - well, some folks called it magic 'cause they didn't know what was happening and I sure wasn't going to trust my secrets to anyone."

Bishop attempted a defense. "Nanny, the territory of your battle grounds and your legion of Maroons can't be compared to the complexity of the ways that the U.S. government with all its hi-tech infiltration methods does battle with revolutionaries who are considered a threat to the status quo."

Wearing her 1900's cloche hat adorned with bright red hibiscus flowers that seemed out of place with her modern day yellow Capri suit, Amy Garvey, an ardent, independent, feminist and activist, stepped forward, faced Bishop, saying, "Nanny knew very well how to protect herself. You think she exposed herself to death from the enemies? Not a chance. She didn't take part in the direct fighting. No, she blessed and directed the campaigns using the Maroon horn, the Abeng, as her means of communication. Bish, rebellions are rebellions no matter where they taking place. Tactics and strategies may differ but it's the leadership that is crucial and Nanny was an outstanding leader."

"Amy, let me raise two points; first, there are many legends surrounding the exploits of Nanny the Maroon and second, my experience with leadership during the Civil rights Movements, enabled me to understand how fluctuating leadership roles can be. Now as for those legends, the one that rings the loudest is your ability to catch bullets with your backside, how so?" spoke up Kwame"
It was Queen Matilda aka Bottom Belly's time. A madras headscarf matched her apron that was worn over a full body white dress. She and her compatriots rarely dressed in clothes other than the ones of their times in 1878. Youthful, robust, buxom, and saucy, it was easy to understand why she commanded leadership.

"Women warriors have a kind of magical power and their exploits frequently become exaggerated, distorted, and taken out of context. Nanny was an Ashanti chieftainess whose history has been kept alive in the African tradition of storytellers. The legend about Nanny and the bullets goes like this: The Maroons strongly believed that Nanny was an "obeah" woman with supernatural powers. A nineteenth century Maroon chief passed down the story of Nantucompong, meaning Nanny takes her back to catch the balls. Nanny, told fifty British soldiers to load their guns and fire on her. She folds back her hands between her legs and catches the fifty shots. Another version is that Nanny would catch the bullets with her buttocks then fart them out. Whichever version you believe the outcome is the same, Nanny was invincible when it came to bullets and British soldiers."

Having said this Matilda crossed her arms across her bosom, squared her shoulders, and firmly planted her bare feet in the lush grass.

"And don't forget the legend about the large cauldron that Nanny kept on the corner of a narrow mountain that was always boiling even though there was no fire under it. British soldiers approaching would look into it fall in and die. We know about curiosity and its consequences and we know how to keep the pot boiling but Nanny knows how to do it better." Queen Mary said this with a defiant- 'I dare you to question me' - look on her smooth, brown, attractive face.

"Now Mr. Kwame Ture, with the given name, Stokely Carmichael, do you want to hear more about our Nanny and legends? But before you answer, I must say that I admire the fact that in 1978 you changed your name to Kwame Ture in honor of your mentors, the Revolutionary African leaders Kwame Nkrumah and Sekou Toure. That was an admirable tribute to your elders."

Kwame nodded in Queen Agnes' direction with appreciation, simultaneously admiring the act of solidarity among the women. "I have great admiration for Nanny's successes regardless of how they are recorded." His male bonding however, urged him to add, "In terms of leadership, Brothers Bish, Walter, and C. L. R. James, each one of them responded to crises with courage and responsibility. It's a shame that all the progress made during your reign, Maurice, has eroded, free medical care, daycare centers and a national maternity law for examples. Sisters, it's true that none of the brothers were considered to have magical or mystical powers but they *were* outstanding leaders."

C. L. R. James who had been silently absorbing the palaver entered in a role that he was accustomed, that of being at the center of Pan African debates and discussions. "The slave trade, slavery, no matter where it took place needs no measuring stick to determine the oppression. In the West Indies, nearly all slaves were branded on their flesh with the particular mark of the owner's estate. The rebel leaders had a common goal –freedom! Many individual slaves sought their own freedom. In Jamaica in the seventeenth century for every two males that escaped there was one female sometimes with young children and infants. The women slaves were advertised as the most "incorrigible" runaways. Too little is known of the exploits, activities, and deviltry of West Indian women warriors and rebels."

"Wha' you mean by deviltry? Cyril Lionel Robert James, yah don bin a Trotskyite, a Marxist, a Trotsky Marxist, a Revolutionary Socialist, a Pan Africanist and a Leninist, now wid all a dat, alla weh know dat de debel himself musta bin at wuk on you sum time or de udder."

"James you got Queen Matilda so worked up that she's reverting to her Crucian dialect", laughed Kwame.

"Nothin' wrong wid a bit of deviltry," Queen Mary added. "Jus' y'all look at Tituba, the African American Native American from Barbados. A Salem minister bring she from Barbados to Massachusetts and Tituba, she continue to practice healin' an' rituals so much so dey call she a witch. Enny time de buckra can't figure out de mind of de Black wimmin dey call dem names like witch, sorceress, possessed or like dey call Nanny, a wuk a magic."

Nanny came to her own defense saying, "Spiritual life was very important to us in every aspect of our lives, from child rearing to military life. All of our slave rebellions involved African spiritual practices. Obeah and in Haiti voodoo, were important and necessary to and for our people. But like Queen Mary say, Western culture, the Colonial rulers, not understanding and being afraid of our culture and us outlawed our practices and gave them a negative meaning, but that didn't stop us. And don't forget the runaways. In spite of all the dangers faced by runaways, women were always found among the slaves who 'pulled foot'. By the way, you St. Croix Queens, you know that some Maroons lived in a mountain cave called 'Maroon's Hole', just east of Ham's Bluff in St. Croix, Virgin Islands. Plenty Maroon villages can be found throughout the Caribbean."

Amy Jacques interjected, "We Caribbean rebel women were called 'rude and contemptuous' by the masters and were considered obstinate and insolent. We women schemed routinely against the property and person of the masters and mistresses and perfected the means by which we could do damage without being found out."

"It doesn't seem as though you've lost that touch."

"Mind your manner brother James. You are in heavenly quarters now, not in the backyard of a rundown house or in a rum shop!", scolded Amy Garvey with a smirk.

Maurice left his recliner selected a golden yellow kidney mango from the fruit bowl and moved closer to the group of women. In between bites and with adept cadences of timing he said, "Brothers, we can consider ourselves lucky this morning with only three queens present. Can you imagine if Queen Cubah, leader of the Jamaican slave uprising in 1760, Queen Breffu, leader of the St. John, V.I. revolt in 1733, and Queen Coziah of St. Thomas, V.I. who led the coal workers in the uprising in 1892, were also present?"

"James, Rodney, Bish, Kwame remember, these women didn't have organizations behind them. There was no SNCC, SCLC, New Jewel Movement, Marxist Party, no suh. Queens Mary, Agnes, and Matilda led the St. Croix labor rebellion of 1878, against the *entire*

Danish government that had refused to make changes in the Labor Act. Mary Thomas was a field worker earning 10 cents a day and when given an allowance of cornmeal and herring everyday, 25 cents was subtracted from the weekly pay. Children and old folks who could not do hard labor earned five cents a day. Queen Mary, tell dese men about dat rebellion."

Given the go ahead from Nanny, Captain Thomas, needed no further urging. "Now I was part of the Fireburn rebellion of 1878. It had its roots in the passing of the Proclamation of 1847 that stated that as of July 1847 new born babies of slaves would be free and all other Black slaves would be free twelve years later. You see, slaves were being freed in other part of the world and the desire for freedom was burning in the bellies of the Virgin Islanders. The Danish gov'ment thought that this proclamation would satisfy the slaves, but no suh! The people did not like the idea that they would be slaves and their children free so they secretly started planning a revolt. Meetings among slaves were forbidden but a skilled craftsman, Moses Gottlieb, known as Buddhoe was the man who secretly organized and led the revolt for freedom in1848. He quietly organized the people and on July 2nd the ringing of the church bells and the blowing of the conch shell around midnight was the signal for the beginning of the rebellion. On July 3d, thousands of people from the country gathered at the Frederiksted Fort shouting for freedom. They told the soldiers at the Fort that if a single shot was fired they would burn all of West End. Finally, the people sent word to Governor-General Peter von Scholten to come to Frederiksted by 4'oclock Monday afternoon or they would burn down the town. The Governor arrived just before 4'oclock and declared, 'All unfree in the Danish West Indies are from today free!'."

"After Emancipation the laborers still had other battles to face. The free Black people had to be paid for their labor but the pay was very low. The Danish West Indian government helped the PLANTERS by passing the Labor Act of 1849. According to dat law laborers had to sign a yearly contract and could change jobs only on contract day. They could not refuse any work that the planters asked of them and had to work for whatever pay given by the planters. Any laborer who did not work was called a vagrant, arrested, and put in jail. As punishment, they had to clean the streets and gutters."

"Every year we were promised that the Labor Act would be repealed, but after t'irty years and still no changes, we had had enough. On October 1, 1878 the laborers came to Frederiksted as they usually did on Contract Day The laborers were gathered at the front of Fort Frederik seeking passes, passports, or requesting changes of jobs They had serious complaints and hoped the Labour Act would be repealed. When they realize that there would be no changes the crowd grew angry and the soldiers tried to make the people go home by waving their sabers. Instead of going home my son, - what a sight -the people started throwing stones, conch shells, bricks, any t'ing deh could get dere hands on. The soldiers ran inside the Fort and started firing dere guns. This only further enraged we. Some tore off the outer gate and t'rew it into the sea. Den dey tried to break da inner gate and the soldiers started shooting again. The crowd broke up and started setting fire to shops, houses, even the Customs house."

"Man that sounds like the fore runner of the scorch earth policy. History repeats itself, Watts, California, and 'burn baby burn'." Kwame said grimly as he listened to Queen Mary.

"You know there were plenty of barrels of rum and kerosene in the shops and houses and when they exploded, - boom, boom, ka-boom, ka-boom, like cannons going off. But we had a strategy. We burned fields and buildings and as we went along and as we met people on the road, we asked, 'Our side? Our side?'"

"What happened to those who didn't join you?"

"Oh, Rodney, dey had sense enough to hide. More than fifty plantations were burned. We lost over one hundred people during that rebellion."

Agnes and Matilda were enthusiastic in their approval of Queen Mary's rendition. Agnes added, "One year after that Fireburn the Labor Act was repealed."

"As long as we accepted the unfair and harsh treatment from the Danish government there would have been no changes," added Matilda. "The laborers of St. Croix decisively demonstrated that they would not be treated as slaves any longer."

Appropriately, Marley's *Redemption Song* was playing, as along the pathway was none other than the Retreat's famed duo.

A chorus of good mornings echoed and Walter offered them fruit and beverages. "Cool coconut water is always welcomed", responded Malcolm as he and his travel companion accepted calabashes filled with delicious coconut water.

"We heard a bit of a ruckus going on as we came to your Quarters. What struggles were being re-enacted this morning?" quipped Malcolm.

"The womenfolk were telling about the Maroon raids and the Fireburn. I was preparing to tell them about history repeating itself when it comes to masters and slaves and necessary rebellions."

Brother Ture", solemnly began Sojourner, "I know a heap of young folks, and old ones who did much for social justice and many who liked to call themselves revo-lu-tion-naries. But I got to say, when it comes to Civil Rights Movement in the USA, you sure got a good story to tell 'bout your role in dat history."

"Kwame, out paths hardly crossed during our lifetimes, you were a rebellious 24 year old member of SNCC, in 1965, the year that I was assassinated. The way I see it is the continuation of the struggle for Black equality, for human rights, for justice for all. We keep coming."

"As young as Kwame was when he arrived, he had played a most significant role, as Sojourner just said, in the Civil Rights Movement. One of the most historically significant and skillfully written autobiographies from that era is <u>Ready for Revolution The Life and Struggles of Stokely Carmichael (Kwame Ture)</u>, by Michael Thelwell. For anyone to claim knowledge, comprehension and understanding of the social movement against racism, without reading this book is a seriously flawed claim." The studious C.L.R. James, comfortably clad in a white guayaberra shirt and tan linen trousers, studied his audience as he settled back in his sun deck chair.

Kwame responded in extremely serious tones. "There has and still exists, so very much mis-understanding concerning social and political nuggets of that era. By that, I mean ideological differences among Black organizations were blown out of proportion by the media. This happened because the dominant white media was ignorant beyond words about the experiences and resulting theories of Black folks. Rebellions in their minds, was automatically equated to lawlessness. Queen Mary Thomas, you spoke about laws forbidding the slaves to meet back in 1847, right?"

"That's right brudder. Buddhoe was a master mind in planning dat rebellion."

"Well let me tell you, in 1965 in Lowndes County, Alabama in a study done by political scientist Charles Hamilton and me, the history of the county showed that Black people could come together for only three things, - sing, pray, and dance. Anytime they came together to do anything else, they were threatened and intimidated. For decades Blacks had been taught that voting, politics is 'white folks' business'."

"Oh, yeah, we too were allowed to have prayer meetings, and at celebrations we danced the quadrille, bamboula and cariso, dances that combined the rhythms of the African drums with European and African melodies and dance steps. But it was at dese very gatherings dat the strategies were planned. The buckra know, but he don't know."

"Kwame", said Amy, "of all the misinterpretations and deliberate falsification of happenings during the movement, I think the most will full distortion was the usage of the term black power. Part of it was ignorance and part of it was fear, but overall, a positive term was turned into a menace."

"That phrase was coined after your arrest; Martin Luther King Jr. wrote his significant Letter from Birmingham Jail; Huey Newton's prison experience made him more militant; and my prison experience turned me into a feared Black Muslim. You would think the police department would get the idea and stop jailing us," said Malcolm with a half smile.

"Brother Malcolm, you are so right. I was arrested for setting up tents on the grounds of the local black high school. When I was released there were about 3000 people there and when I appeared there was a huge roar, which I acknowledged with a clenched- fist salute. I clearly remember it all. 'This is the twenty seventh time I've been arrested and I ain't going to jail no more!' There was an explosion of cheers and clapping. 'The only way we're gonna stop them white men from whupping us is to take over. We've been saying freedom for six years and we ain't got nothing. What we're gonna start saying now is black power!' At this point SNCC member Willie Ricks shouted out, "What do you want?" "Black power" the crowd yelled back in unison. In my mind black power simply meant getting political power for black people. You know, Black people coming together to form a political force, to elect representatives to speak for them. I saw it as an economic and physical bloc needed to enforce our political clout." *(Quotes from Thelwell's biography of Ture)*

"And in a typical fashion the media translated it into something dangerous and fearful that should be stamped out. They began equating "black power" with violence, Black Nationalism, even

91

calling it racism. TIME magazine called it the 'new racism'."
Amy shook her head as she spoke.

"Speaking of Black people initiating, galvanizing, and confronting
the establishment, Brother Malcolm your account of the 1963 civil
rights March on Washington gave a totally different story than the
one the media and most historians presented and told to the
public."

"Rodney, I would say what is SOLD to the public", countered
Malcolm.

C.L.R. James with a radiant smile bantered Malcolm, "But brother
you likened the March to a picnic with folks in a joyful mood,
dangling their feet in a 'pond' and waving banners and delivering
well mannered hopeful speeches."

Returning the grin Malcolm answered, "I was simply giving an
analysis of how a Black initiative with a strong, demonstrative,
militant plan of action, can become adulterated to the extent that
the original meaning and purpose becomes lost."

"I know exactly what Malcolm means," said Kwame. "The
original plan was to march on the White House and virtually shut
down political traffic, demanding the President to act on the
passage of the Civil Rights Bill. Instead, the marchers marched
between the Washington Memorial and the Lincoln Memorial—
two dead presidents—and we never got to see the living president.
And it's true, the March WAS redesigned and orchestrated by
white liberals."

"But what happened to all your big male leaders? We rebel
wimmin keep telling you men folk who call yourselves leaders that
you don't know how to deal wit buckras."

"You're right on track, Queen Mary Thomas. The Big Six, that's
the so-called Negro leaders of the March, allowed the government
infiltrators to tell them when, where and how to arrive and be sure

to leave town by sundown and believe me you, 'dey sho nuff did'." Malcolm chuckled in spite of himself and continued. "Let me shed an additional bit of info about that government controlled March. The signs the marchers carried, the songs they sang, and even their speeches— were all dictated by the White House. John Lewis who was chair of SNCC at the time, and currently the only living member of that group of so-called Black leaders, wanted to give a speech attacking the Kennedy administration for its duplicity on civil rights. He was not allowed to deliver his original speech. His speech was censored by the Catholic Archbishop of Washington, D.C., Rt. Rev. Patrick O'Boyle. But even watered down, Lewis' speech was the most radical and therefore most controversial."

"So, now wait", began Nanny a bit perplexed. "You telling me that all the glory and greatness of the March on Washington was nothing more than a popysho? Somet'ing in de mortar besides de pestle, eh? And who were deh 'Big Six?'"

"Oh it was quite a show. About 250,000 people, a quarter of whom were white. It was the largest demonstration seen in the nation's capital and the first to have extensive television coverage. The Big Six were: James Farmer of the Congress of Racial Equality (CORE); John Lewis of the Student Nonviolent Coordinating Committee (SNCC); A. Phillip Randolph of the Brotherhood of the Sleeping Car Porters (BSCP); Roy Wilkins of the National Association for the Advancement of Colored People (NAACP); Whitney Young, Jr. of the National Urban League (NUL); Martin Luther King, Jr. of the Southern Christian Leadership Conference (SCLC)," rattled off Kwame without missing a beat.

"Not a woman among them. When you men going to learn that as long as you exclude women from leadership roles, somewhere down the road you doomed for failure?!" Amy gave a satisfying nod of her head as she completed her words.
"For clarification let me add that James Farmer was imprisoned in Louisiana at the time and his speech was read by Floyd McKissick. The one female speaker was Josephine Baker, who introduced

several "Negro Women Fighters for Freedom", including Rosa Parks. Oh, there were entertainers, artists, musical performances by Marian Anderson, Joan Baez, Mahalia Jackson, James Baldwin read a speech, Harry Belafonte and Ossie Davis were there,-like I said, a party atmosphere, -it ceased to be a Black angry, militant, impatient March. It was infiltrated by whites, not integrated by whites," concluded Malcolm.

"What a pistacle," schupps Nanny.

There were disquieting movements among the Islanders as Nanny's words sunk in. Finally, Maurice Bishop spoke out.

"The March like all events and happenings during the Movement played important roles particularly in terms of learning from our experiences. The business of intra-group conflict was something that took at times as much energy and emotional stress than direct contact with the opposition. The bitter arguments, those faint of heart, the egos, the accommodationists,- these intra-group struggles were overwhelming but we persevered, there was no other choice."

"And through it all" grinned Bishop, "my buddy, Stokely Kwame Carmichael Ture, became a star."

"Bish, I certainly don't want my legacy to be branded with a star quality. I want to be remembered as a Pan Africanist, an activist, a fighter for the freedom of my people."

Sojourner attempted to bring closure of some sort to the discussion by saying, "Son it is important that people know of the courageous, precarious, humanitarian life you lived. All along, you didn't separate the political from da personal. The time you spent in Mississippi, Alabama, Cuba or Conakry, your basic true revolutionary feelings, and principles remained steadfast and admirable. And your bit of wimminizing, well dat only made you human according to patriarchy."

Nanny who had been listening intently came out with, "Sister Sojourner, tell me more about patriarchal wimminizing. Is that something new?"

Malcolm quickly said, "Next time around Nanny. Right now Sister Sojourner and I have to keep moving along."

Sojourner smiled appreciatively knowing her explanation would start another challenge of wits, she walked over to Malcolm, took his arm and they made their good byes, with Malcolm selecting two delicious grafted mangoes from the bowl.

They departed Caribbean Corners, they passed water fountains emerging from bamboo shoots creating the constant gurgling sounds that mingled harmoniously with the Marley sounds, and they inhaled the scent of teas from the various herbal plants. Pleasing the eyes were various palms and large elephant ear plants with vines and drift wood artistically arranged amidst the greenery.

Chapter Five Glossary and Endnotes

- *Bob Marley (1945-1981):* Birth name- Robert Nesta Marley. Born in Saint Ann Parish, Jamaica. A singer, songwriter, guitarist and activist, whose mother was a black Jamaican and father a white Jamaican, a Marine officer as well as a plantation overseer. Bob Marley is a known performer of reggae music, a faithful Rastafarian and is regarded by many as a prophet of the religion. His posthumous compilation album, *Legend* (1984) is the best selling reggae album ever with sales over 12 million copies.
- *Huey Newton   (1942-1987)*: Co-founder with Bobby Seale of the Black Panther Party for Self Defense, an African-American organization established to promote Civil Rights and self-defense. He was born in Louisiana and moved to Oakland, California with his family. He was illiterate when he graduated from high school but taught himself how to read. As a result of his activism he was targeted by the government and was shot to death in a raid.
- *Cariso or Caruso*: A type of music that combines the rhythms of the African drums with European and African melodies, usually played during Caribbean Christmas and New Year festivities.
- *"Bukra"*: A West Indian word used for the white man, particularly the planter.
- *"Knocking dog"*: A West Indian term used to denote abundance and plenty.
- *"Popysho"*: Originally derived from the phrase "puppet show". A West Indian word meaning foolishness, nonsense, stupidity or behavior without real merit.
- *"Pistacle"*: A West Indian word denoting chaos and foolishness.
- *"Schupps"*: A West Indian word indicating the sound of one sucking their teeth. An implication of disgust, annoyance or rejection. It is an expression usually used by adults and considered rude behavior when done by children.

GRENADA: This Invasion Was Not Televised

Johnnetta B. Cole and Gloria I. Joseph

On the 25th of October, 1983, 1,900 Marines, paratroopers, and Rangers supported by heavy artillery, tanks, and the most sophisticated weaponry, descended upon Grenada, a sovereign Black state whose entire military force consisted of 2,000 men and women. By the height of the invasion three days later, the US military presence had swelled to 6,000. The mission, ostensibly, to rescue 600 medical students and 400 other US citizens from the tiny Caribbean island, where chaos and confusion reigned following the assassination of Prime Minister Maurice Bishop and six members of his cabinet. But it is the private mission and the undisclosed purposes of the US invasion that remain to be carefully examined.

Questions abound. Why were most US allies not informed of the invasion beforehand, and why were the grave reservations expressed by the prime minister of Great Britain, the US government's most trusted ally, ignored? Why was the press denied its right to witness, describe, and investigate, on behalf of the American people, a full-scale military invasion? What does the invasion of Grenada portend for US foreign policy and action in other parts of our hemisphere and the world? And what does all of this tell us about the values, attitudes, and morality of the leadership of our country?

Why an Invasion? Public and Private Reasons

Let us begin at the beginning. When Ronald Reagan came before this nation to announce that the invasion of Grenada had begun, he stated that the US was responding to a plea for intervention made by the Organization of Eastern Caribbean States. What he didn't state, however, was that the OECS treaty demands unanimity in all its decisions and that only five of its eight signatories agreed to the invasion – St. Kitts-Nevis, Montserrat, and, of course, Grenada, did not. Additionally, the OECS treaty could be invoked only defensively – that is, only if Grenada had been preparing to launch an invasion of another island.

What we are left to ponder is an unprovoked invasion, launched on the questionable authority of a treaty to which the US is not even a signatory. Even more important, by in-

Johnnetta B. Cole is Visiting Professor of Anthropology at Hunter College, New York; Gloria Joseph is Professor of Social Work at Hampshire College, Massachusetts. Both are active with the U.S.-Grenada Friendship Society. Professor Cole is on the U.S. Peace Council's National Advisory Board

vading Grenada the US unequivocally violated treaties to which it is a signatory – the charters of the UN and the OAS, both of which specifically prohibit the use of military force.

According to President Reagan, there were two main reasons for the invasion: to "rescue" Americans supposedly trapped on the island and in danger of being taken hostage; and to prevent a Cuban occupation. But were Americans and the island itself – really in danger, or was the Reagan administration merely exploiting the turbulent situation that existed in Grenada at that moment, in order to return the island to the US "sphere of influence"?

A critically important – and revealing – event took place in 1981 that is worth recalling here. At that time the United States conducted its largest naval maneuvers since WW II. In these "war games," the US Navy was to invade the fictitious, leftist Caribbean island of "Amber" to install a "favorable" regime. (In a message to the UN at the time of these maneuvers, Prime Minister Bishop charged that the exercises were a "practice run" for a direct invasion of Grenada by US troops. Bishop also asked for an explanation of the maneuvers in a official letter to President Reagan, a request that went unanswered.)

That the 1983 "rescue" of American students was merely a pretext for the invasion is demonstrated by the fact that the US forces were not trained to rescue but in search and destroy missions; that they didn't know where the students were or that there were two schools on the island, and that they didn't even approach the schools until the second day of the invasion. The students were, of course, unharmed. Additionally, as Hedrick Smith reported in the October 29 edition of the *New York Times*, on the day preceding the invasion the curfew on the island had been relaxed and the airport reopened; indeed, at least four charter planes left Grenada that day with Americans among those on board.

It should also be noted that those who had taken power in Grenada gave the US government a specific guarantee of the safety of all Americans on the island; the government of Cuba informed the US that according to its reports, no US or foreign citizen was in danger and expressed "readiness to cooperate so that the problems could be resolved without violence or intervention." Finally, 300 parents of the US medical students appealed to the President not to invade and thereby jeopardize the lives of their children. But despite all these assurances and appeals, the Reagan administration chose not to use established international procedures for evacuating individuals from troubled areas. Aggression overpowered diplomacy.

Cuba and the Airstrip

Some days after the invasion was launched, President Reagan proudly announced that "We got there just in time" to prevent Cuban occupation of Grenada, that the island "was a Soviet Cuban colony being readied as a major military bastion to export terror and undermine democracy." He said that US military forces were "staggered by the depth and strength of the Cuban military presence on the island," that it was far greater than the 800 construction workers, medical workers and diplomatic personnel Cuba acknowledged having on Grenada. But as the hullaballoo over the invasion died down, the Defense Department quietly admitted that the Cuban estimate of the presence of 784 of its people on the island was accurate, and that, indeed no more than 10 per cent of them could possibly be characterized as military personnel.

But never mind all that, urged the State Department. Regardless of the number of Cubans in Grenada, the *real* danger was the 10,000 foot airstrip which the Cuban government and people were helping to build on the island. On October 27, 1983, while the invasion was underway, Reagan said that the Grenadian airport "looked suspiciously suitable for military aircraft, including Soviet-built, long-range bombers. Six months earlier, on March 23, he claimed "Cubans, with Soviet financing and backing, are in the process of building an airfield with a 10,000 foot runway." In fact, the airport was being built because of a report made several years ago by the World Bank, in which it was found that Grenada would have to increase its tourist trade if it was ever to have a solvent economy. The airport, being built to accommodate the potential increase in tourism, had received

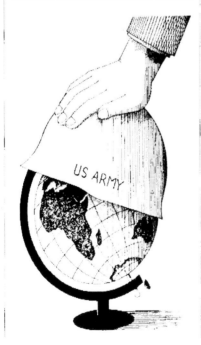

US ARMY

at least half of its financing from US allies in western Europe. In fact, the Cubans who worked on it did so under the supervision of the Plessey Corporation of Great Britain. Further, a November 27 report on Cable Network News stated that US transport planes had already damaged the airstrip, which, the report implied, could never have been intended for heavy military hardware, a fact confirmed by representatives of the Plessey firm.

Another complete distortion of facts: the "enormous supply" of weapons found by military personnel in six warehouses on the island. When journalists were finally allowed to view the "arsenal," supposedly provided by Cuba, they discovered two warehouses less than half full, one less than a quarter full, one filled with kitchen equipment, another with food, and another empty. Most of the weapons were out-of-date rifles, some more than a century old. Heavy equipment consisted of four mortars.

"Secret" documents found in the rubble of the invasion that the Administration used to "prove" the Cuban-Soviet take over of Grenada showed, on careful reading, a Cuban agreement to send Grenada 27 *soldiers for training purposes* and a total military aid package from the USSR of $37 million over five years. That works out to just over seven million dollars a year, about what the US spends *daily* in Central America, or the annual cost of the police department in any modest US town. Moreover, that the Bishop government needed a national defense was spelled out most clearly by the invasion itself.

It has also been widely rumored that Cuba was behind the murder of Maurice Bishop. This is yet another example of how the US government manipulated information concerning events in Grenada. In fact, Prime Minister Bishop had strong ties to Cuba and Fidel Castro. Castro declared three days of mourning in his country after the death of Bishop and his six cabinet members. And when General Austin, who staged the coup, made a request to Cuba for assistance against the US invasion, Castro denied him aid stating that the request "was not easy to grant after the things that have happened in that country."

The American people have been lied to time and again concerning the invasion of Grenada. And our government managed to get away with these lies due to an unprecedented abridgement of one of our fundamental rights – freedom of the press. All news concerning the invasion of Grenada was controlled by the Reagan administration. During the initial stages, news correspondents were entirely barred from the island, and when entry was finally permitted, all reports were screened by the Department of Defense. In fact, it was a Canadian reporter who revealed that 47 helpless people were killed in the US bombing of a mental hospital on the island. (The Pentagon acknowledges 17 deaths.) With little more than a shrug of the shoulders, the administration in Washington instituted this alarming censorship of information.

Thus, the Reagan administration consciously manipulated realities – from the way in which the US choreographed its "invited entry" into Grenada to its reckoning of the number and purpose of Cubans in that country, to denial of media access to Grenada, to withholding information on the bombing of a mental hospital, to the counting of civilian deaths resulting from the invasion – in order to prepare public opinion to accept what was, in fact, a blatant violation of international law and an offense against human morality.

American Expansionism

There is a long and bi-partisan history of US expansion into Central America and the Caribbean. With the attitude that Caribbean islands are the U.S.' backyard, our government has sent marines, assassins and CIA agents, and assisted capitalist firms and even pop culture to intervene into the affairs of our American neighbors. In a recent review of Walter LaFeber's book, *Inevitable Revolutions*, Alfred Stepan summarizes the history of US expansionism in the Americas in these terms:

the Marines were dispatched to Central America and the Caribbean no fewer than 20 times between 1898 and 1920 alone. The invasion of Grenada two weeks ago was only the latest such example . . . [and] almost every liberal 20th century President has had an "adventure" in Central America . . .

Woodrow Wilson not only sent Marines to Haiti, Nicaragua and the Dominican Republic, but more importantly, crafted the extension of the Monroe Doctrine known as the Wilson Corollary, which was meant to exclude European finance and construction activity from Latin America. This corollary had almost no effect in South America but contributed to the overwhelming economic presence of the United States in Central America. Mr LaFeber examines Franklin D. Roosevelt's policies on banking, military aid and support of dictatorships and concludes, "The Good Neighbor carried on interventionism in Central America and tightened the system far beyond anything Theodore Roosevelt and Woodrow Wilson could imagine." John F. Kennedy not only launched the Bay of Pigs invasion of Cuba but shifted assistance policy, encouraging Latin American armies to make counterinsurgency their fundamental mission. Lyndon Johnson buried the Alliance for Progress and intervened in the Dominican Republic. Jimmy Carter, not Ronald Reagan, began our current involvement in El Salvador. (*New York Times Book Review*, October 6, 1983.)

Despite worldwide denunciation of the events in Grenada only a US veto blocked the UN Security Council from a declaration condemning the act; the UN General Assembly voted 108 to 9 to deplore the invasion; the Organization of American States called the invasion a violation of treaty agreements—the Reagan administration successfully, if temporarily, managed to orchestrate the emotions (and jingoism) of the American people. How can this be? How can so many people in this country accept the flimsy, ever-shifting rationale offered by the administration for this invasion?

Unfortunately, certain attitudes that have become ingrained in our society—anti-Communism, racism, sexism, and national chauvinism—were very much alive in the invasion of Grenada. Each of these attitudes requires some examination.

Anti-Communism

One of the most powerful tenets of US foreign policy is a phobic dread of communism. If asked to explain and define communism as an economic system and an ideology, it is not likely that most Americans could do so. As Adrienne Rich points out in *Ms.* magazine (October 28, 1983):

We have spent forty years as a people—the whole of many people's lives—immersed in Cold War rhetoric, images of a brutish and virulent communism whose hostility is our most urgent national burden. Most of us have grown up with messages telling us to focus on the enemy without, not on the violence and indifference our government visits on its own citizens, the manic self-assertion of privilege it defines as "national interest." In a strange way the U.S. has been for decades deep-frozen in the Cold War, unable to move freely

and responsively in the currents of history.

It is important to note that throughout the invasion of Grenada, reference was never made to the accomplishments of the Grenadian revolution under the leadership of Maurice Bishop, a Marxist. We briefly enumerate here a list of the major achievements of the Grenadian Revolution since March 13, 1979, when Maurice Bishop and the New Jewel Movement came to power in a bloodless coup that ended years of despotic and corrupt rule by Eric Gairy:

1. Reduction and stabilization of food prices and other essential commodities.
2. Creation of the Agro/Industrial Sector and new jobs in the education, health, and tourism sectors.
3. High quality free medical care.
4. Elimination of school fees (traditional in Caribbean societies). Free books and school uniforms for those most needy.
5. A massive campaign to wipe out illiteracy.
6. A National Maternity Law, stipulating two months leave with pay for all female workers.
7. The establishment of day care centers throughout the entire country.
8. People's Power participation in mass organizations of women, youth, and workers.
9. Public participation in the development of the national budget.
10. Increase in delivery of social services for all Grenadians.
11. The creation of a popular militia and People's Revolutionary Army to protect Grenadian people.
12. Legal equality for all Grenadians in pay and social status regardless of race, gender, or class background.
13. The rapid elimination and prosecution of cases of discrimination inherited from the colonial and neo-colonial periods.
14. Continued construction of an international airport, to revitalize a decaying tourist industry, the island's main foreign exchange earner.
15. A decrease in unemployment from 49 percent in 1979 to 13 percent in 1983.
16. A decrease in food imports by 12 percent during 1983; four new agricultural training schools were opened in 1982, subsistence food production doubled from 1981-1982.

Now, as a mere sideline to the rescue of those supposedly endangered US students, our government rationalizes its role in the setting up of a new (pro-US) government on the island by claiming to have reinstated democracy there. In fact, the US invasion has put an end to four years of tremendous progress in Grenada. As the Cleveland *Plain Dealer* reported on Nov. 11, "Governor General Sir Paul Scoon [formerly the British representative to Grenada] is using powers he gave himself last week to let soldiers of the invading force detain Grenadians, man roadblocks and search without warrant . . . Scoon is also empowered under the emergency proclamation to authorize preventive detention, press censorship and bans on public processions, and to let police and occupying troops make arrests without warrant . . . The state of emergency was proclaimed under the 1973 constitution and a 1970 law, both written before Grenada gained independence from Great Britain."

This striking display of hypocrisy goes hand in hand with our government's support of the totally anti-democratic regimes in South Africa, Haiti, South Korea, the Philippines, Honduras, Guatemala, Chile, and other fascistic states that happen to support the US.

And lest we forget that the invasion, occupation, and domination of Grenada by US forces is intimately connected with the Reagan Administration's plans for Central America and the Caribbean, on November 18, just 3 weeks after the invasion, 1,000 US Marines and 500 Honduran infantrymen staged a mock Grenada-style assault on a Honduran beach in maneuvers that Nicaragua charges are a prelude to an invasion. Prime Minister Bishop's 1981 message to the UN should not be forgotten. All that seems to matter to Washington is the extent to which the interests of the US business communi-

ty, and the military-industrial complex are met.

Racism

The invasion of the sovereign Black nation of Grenada cannot be divorced from a history of US aggression and genocidal practices against peoples of color around the world. The decimation of the Native American peoples, the enslavement of the descendants of Africa, the annexation of half of Mexico and the Caribbean, the gunboat diplomacy used throughout the Americas over the past century, the bombing of Hiroshima and Nagasaki, to the killings of Black American males by police (the number of Black men in America who have been killed by police bullets is greater than the number of people killed by guns in Northern Ireland) - all are part of a racist legacy that distorts the political history of the United States.

Pacific News Service

Little attention has been given to the racist nature of the invasion of Grenada. The absence of any report by the Pentagon or the press of Grenadian casualties suffered in the invasion makes crystal clear how dearly Grenadian lives are cherished in Washington. Later reports have indicated at least 200 Grenadian civilian deaths; military casualties are still unknown or unreported. Before the October incidents, how many American people even knew where Grenada was? (It was days before newscasters learned that Grenada – Gre-NAY-da – is not pronounced Gran-AH-da, as is a city in southern Spain.) How is it possible for the white people of our country to be manipulated into cheering for a war against a people they've never heard of if not because of a deep-seated chauvinism toward the non-white peoples of the world?

The projection by the media of the Marines as welcomed liberators of the Grenadian people is in the same vein as the once-held image of missionaries and slavers being the great white saviors of the souls and societies of Black African heathens. Without referring to the inevitable confusion and fear of the Grenadian people following the assassination of their leader and the ensuing martial law, and the uncertainty of what would follow under the administration of those who carried out that coup, the expression of relief that the massive US presence evoked was portrayed and interpreted as a childlike adoration of the great white fathers. And of course, no reference was ever made to the psychological warfare teams that prepared the island for the "welcome." In the *New York Times* (Nov. 9, 1983) Michael T. Kaufman wrote that posters were

> prepared and pasted up in town [St. George's] by a United States army psychological operations unit flown here from Fort Bragg in North Carolina last week.

> One poster shows photographs of Mr. Coard and Gen. Hudson Austin, the man who took over control of the Military Council after the shooting, at Fort Rupert. The heavyset general is shown seated, wearing only a towel around his waist and looking downcast.

> Beyond him stands an American soldier. The image is one of humiliation and the text on the poster proclaims: "These criminals attempted to sell Grenada out to the Communists. Now they have surrendered. The Grenadian people will never again allow such characters to assume power and cause such hardship. Support democracy in Grenada."

Sexism, Chauvinism and Arrogance

From the moment that the US people were made privy to our government's decision to invade Grenada, right up to the patriotic homecoming of some of the invading forces, the public was exposed to one grand display of male supremacy. The individuals who consulted with a pajamaed president in the wee hours of the morning on October were all white men. The personnel who determined the fate of Grenadians were white men. (This is not to suggest, however, that had there been women in key positions in the State Department, the Pentagon, and the Oval Office, such an invasion would not have occurred. Indeed, Jeanne Kirkpatrick and Eugenia Charles were accomplices to the crime.) Nevertheless, it is largely a male crew that sits in Washington playing the role of world policeman.

The portrayal in the media of the landing of the Marines was the epitome of the aggressive, penetrating, conquering he-man, which served as a "call to arms" to many young American men who lined up in substantial numbers at their local marine recruiting offices during the invasion and afterward.

When Mr. Reagan was asked his reaction to the UN General Assembly vote deploring the invasion, he commented: "that news didn't upset my breakfast." It has long been the position of the Reagan administration that the UN is overrun with Third World nations (read: peoples of color). One should compare Reagan's flippant remarks concerning the General Assembly's vote with the conciliatory tone with which members of his administration responded to criticisms from western (read: white) allies.

The Reagan administration was surely playing upon a US sense of defeat and need for victory as it invaded one of the smallest lands in the Americas. With the defeat of US forces in Vietnam; the crisis involving American hostages in Iran; the 30-year survival of the Cuban Revolution despite a US economic blockade and both overt and covert interventions; and the triumph of the Sandinistas in Nicaragua; and coming just days after the bombing of the US Marine base in Beirut, the invasion of Grenada was used at least partially to restore American confidence in its power and might to end the "Vietnam syndrome," to restore American "supremacy." As Sen. Lawton Chiles (D-Fla.) remarked, "One day we've got the number of Marine deaths which shocked us all, and the next day we find we are invading Grenada. As somebody said are we looking for a war we can win?"

Even though the conquest of this tiny nation is hardly a triumph in which to glory, it has left the American military establishment basking in hero worship, its first such emotionalism in the better part of two decades. Nobody is loving it more than the Rangers, the lightly equipped, fast-hitting shock troops who did most of the hard fighting in Grenada. "It's great to feel wanted," said Sgt. Tracy Hickman, a 23-year-old Ranger from Las Vegas who said he knocked out a Cuban mortar position in the Grenada fighting. The *New York Times* (Nov. 22, 1983) reported, "America loves a winner," said First Sgt. William Acebes, one of the United States Army Rangers who returned here recently from Grenada. "When I came home from Vietnam I was treated like dirt. I even left the army at one point because I was so discouraged. But now ... now I walk down the street and people slap me on the back and say 'Thanks.' You go into a bar and suddenly everybody wants to buy you a drink."

Today, the United States continues to occupy Grenada and to carry out classic colonial practices. As one reporter describes the scenes:

> Uniformed soldiers and State Department people are sweeping the entire island for arms and resisters or their sympathizers. The Caribbean Peacekeeping Force (CPF) made up primarily of the American 82nd Airborne Division, can be seen entering homes and shops or arresting people without warrants. A psychological warfare group from Fort Bragg, North Carolina, is broadcasting "Spice Island Radio" and leafleting the country with admonitions to "turn in the PRG." (*Village Voice*, November 22, 1983.)

Many of the people who are arrested, without warrants, are taken prisoner, held in a camp, and interrogated. The *New York Times* (Nov. 22, 1983) reported that more than 1,100 Grenadians and Cubans had been interrogated:

> The camp and its five towers are on a peninsula on the southwest corner of the island. ... Beyond the control gate and barbed wire, and between two clusters of tents, are the most prominent features of the camp: two rows of newly constructed wooden chambers, each measuring about eight feet by eight feet.

> In one cluster are the interrogation booths, with open doors and two chairs. During an inspection tour today, reporters saw American intelligence personnel, clipboards and yellow legal pads in hand, interviewing prisoners.

> Beside them, however, were 10 isolation booths, each with four small windows and a number of ventilation holes with a radius of half an inch. Prisoners must enter these booths by crawling through a hatch that extends from the floor of the booths to about knee level. The booths have foam mattresses.

> Once the prisoners are inside, the hatches are locked. Prisoners are permitted two half-hour exercise periods daily. Inside one of the chambers, someone, apparently a prisoner, had written, "It's not in here."

Another View

While the *Reagan* Administration played on the anti-communism, racism, sexism, and national chauvinism of certain segments of the American populace, the invasion also brought out demonstrators, initiated teach-ins, rallies, and telegram campaigns, and inspired angry leaders and articles. For example, the New York City police estimated that on October 27, 10,000 protesters, mobilized by word of mouth overnight, marched for almost four hours through midtown Manhattan.

And while it came as no surprise that the majority of the 14 congressmen who carried out an investigation in Grenada managed to rationalize the invasion, three members of the team (including two members of the Congressional Black Caucus) voiced dissenting opinions. If the rescue of 1000 American citizens from Grenada was our objective, Rep. Ronald V. Dellums of California asked, why are we still there?

As the *New York Times* reported on November 11, seven Democratic representatives asked the House of Representatives to impeach President Reagan for ordering the invasion of Grenada.

> A draft resolution, shown to reporters before its introduction, said Mr. Reagan's action had been unconstitutional and thus an impeachable offense because it has usurped the power of Congress the declare war, ignored treaty obligations, and violated First Amendment rights in preventing the press from covering the invasion in its first few days. Those submitting the resolution were Ted Weiss of New York, John Conyers, Jr., of Michigan, Julian C. Dixon and Mervyn M. Dymally of California, Henry B. Gonzalez and Mickey Leland of Texas, and Parren Mitchell or Maryland.

While the Reagan administration carefully focused public attention on events taking place in Grenada, some Americans were mindful that at home, during the days of the invasion,

- Ronald Reagan fired his critics on the U.S. Civil Rights Commission;
- the right to federally funded abortions was being voted away;
- Ronald Reagan made the headlines for grudgingly signing a bill making Martin Luther King Jr.'s birthday a national holiday, and then flying off to play golf at a segregated course in Georgia;
- the Pentagon began to ship first-strike cruise and Pershing II nuclear missiles to Europe, despite overwhelming public opposition on that continent;
- preparations for a US-sponsored or direct invasion of El Salvador and Nicaragua continued;
- and in New York City, the financial and cultural capital of the richest country in the world, 40,000 men, women and children continue to pick through the garbage cans for their daily food, and to sleep in the doorways of public buildings at night.

The unconscionable behavior of those who participated in the assassination of Prime Minister Bishop, six members of his government, and labor leaders has received world condemnation. But the hidden agenda of the US government, which seeks to destroy all enemies of corporate America, must also be condemned, most vociferously by the US peace forces. No matter how unstable the internal affairs of Grenada were following the bloody coup, the restoration of order and the solution of domestic problems must rest in the hands of the Grenadian people themselves. The details of what led to the coup have yet to be fully disclosed, and until 'the jury is in' we must focus all our attention on this reality: our country invaded another and displayed enough provocation and illegality to put the entire world in an extremely heightened state of tension and danger. Regardless of how one views Cuba or the Soviet Union, we must recognize that if it were not for the constraint displayed by these nations in the face of repeated provocations and unlawful actions by the Reagan administration, the invasion of Grenada could have signaled the beginning of a much wider war, with potentially catastrophic results for the peoples of the earth, not least of all our own.

The conclusions being drawn publicly by the Reagan Administration and its supporters in the media — that we have put Vietnam behind us," that we have shown we are not a "paper tiger," that the US armed forces are now prepared to restore preferred regimes elsewhere around the world — are dangerous in the extreme. This glorious victory of the mightiest military machine the world has seen over the poorest, smallest nation in the world, with its tiny militia (already demoralized after the murder of its national leaders) aided by a relative handful of poorly-armed foreign construction workers is hardly the stuff from which legends are made. As a matter of fact, to the extent that the published reports are accurate, the elephant and the flea suffered roughly equal casualties. To draw encouragement from this episode for an invasion of, say, Nicaragua, with its three million people armed and ready to fight, is to send the US people into another Vietnam, with its body bags, atrocities, slaughter and corrosion of spirit (not to mention erosion of our liberties).

Conclusion

Our mandate is clear: First we must demand and work for the withdrawal of all US armed forces and personnel from Grenada — something that, according to Ronald Reagan, was to happen within five days of the invasion — and the return of self-determination to the Grenadian people. Our on-going task is to intensify our struggle against the aggressive, militarist policies of the Reagan Administration and the corporate circles on whose behalf it acts. What is at stake is nothing less than the right of sovereignty for every nation, and the right of every human being to live in a world of peace.

We are grateful to Marva Wexler and Wendy Fisher for their assistance in the preparation of this article

Chapter   VI

Musician's   Mansion

'Polymorphous Perverse' is the name Tupac Shakur gave to Musicians Mansions. The compositions of the various characters and their peculiar styles as well as the ornate multi- colored buildings made the name extremely appropriate. Not all of the inhabitants were revolutionaries according to the "Retreat" definition but the musicians being a carefree group welcomed all new comers.

Tupac Shakur and Mahalia Jackson were comfortably seated on what the residents called 'musical chairs' and it was easy to see the origin of the name. The benches and chairs, haphazardly spaced on the front lawn of the two-tiered building were black and white and designed like musical bars, clefts, and notes. Twenty-five year old Tupac, and sixty-one year old Mahalia, had become close friends shortly after Tupac's arrival in September 1996. Mahalia had a motherly attraction and a special interest in the young man whose name, life, and music were initially a total puzzlement to her. The community affectionately referred to them as the odd couple, but Mahalia and Tupac drew energy from their differences and used that energy for inspirational dialogue.

Mahalia wore a wrap around skirt, aquamarine with yellow block prints at the top and bottom, which was fashionable at the time of her arrival in1972. A white embroidered blouse fit her rotund figure as comfortably as did her rocking chair. She was facing Tupac who was seated across from her at a small, round wrought iron table.

She looked fondly at his clean-shaven head, nose ring, and bushy eyebrows and thought about how at one time his songs were denigrating and demeaning to women and how his music had changed to politically uplifting messages. She tapped her fingers on the table, and said, "Tupac, I want to hear it straight from your

103

mouth, one more time, your belief that I could be a great rap artist with my gospel songs."

"Ma Halie, yes, I *know* that you could rap gospel and I can even hear your first platinum rap recording of, "Moving on Up a Little Higher." When you recorded it in 1948, it was so hot that stores couldn't keep enough copies to meet the demand. It may sound outlandish at first, - Mahalia rapping, - but look at it from this perspective. Rapping in its simplest sense is style of music - a rhythmic, rhyming vocal style, with a background beat and scratching performed on a turntable by a DJ. Now the words or lyrics of the vocalist tells a story or describes lifestyles. Now poems and stories can be set to music like operettas, operas, and Broadway musicals."

Somewhat perplexed, Mahalia said, "Now you're telling me that rap can be likened to opera? I wonder what Paul Robeson would have to say about that.'

"Paul Robeson, now that is one fantastic Black man, and to think he is now my neighbor. He was one of the true bass voices, as well as baritone, in America, - a terrific athlete, an actor, and above all a fearless fighter for rights, peace and justice throughout the world. He used his music to spread his belief and spirituals were part of his repertoire. We can talk more about him later, for now let me further explain why a rapping Mahalia is not as far-fetched as it sounds."

"Before you go any further let me say that I think it would be sacrilegious for me to do rapping. Remember, Tupac, I took a solemn vow, and never broke it, to never sing secular music. That vow cost me my first marriage because of my husband's repeated pressure for me to do so. I was offered a lot of money to go secular, but I refused and he left."

Tupac fingered his single strand cowrie necklace and loosened the top button of the jacket to his loose fitting two-piece dark brown outfit. "Ma Halie, I am not suggesting that you sing the material of

104

the rappers. I'm saying that your gospel songs could be set to rap. Let's look at music, songs, and poetry in an historical sense starting with the griots of West Africa. The storytellers, accompanied by a few musical instruments traveled from village to village telling their stories. This practice was similar to the medieval singers and musicians in Greek antiquity the ancient string instrument the lyre accompanied the singer: the Celtic minstrel, the bards, were poets voicing heroic themes; and the opera, stories set to music for singers and instrumentalists. What does all this tell us?"

"I still ain't heard why I could, should do rapping."
"Let me finish. With rap or hip-hop-"

"Tupac, so now we hip hopping. My dancing days long been over," Mahalia chortled as she slapped her hand on the table.

"Mom, we're talking about music in an elaborate sense. Hip-hop music is a style of popular music with a rhythmic rhyming vocal style called rapping and also known as emceeing. In the background are rhythms or melodies. It can be performed a cappella but it's more common to have rappers with a DJ or live band providing an appropriate beat. Technically rapping refers to the practice of speaking poetically over rhythms or melodies and hip-hop includes rapping plus break dancing."

"Tupac, you back to that dancing, but what troubles me about rap is the sinful words, the bad language, the terrible talk about women and drugs and I guess gangsters because they call it gangsta rap don't they? And half the time I can't understand what they're saying. Sometimes it sounds like a whole lot of chanting and panting, ranting and repetitions and most of the times I can't understand a word they're saying"

Unsuppressed laughter exploded from Tupac. From one of the opened windows of the mansion embellished with curlicues and with soundproof rooms, came the unmistakable rough and aggressive voice of 'Big Mama' Willie Mae Thornton.

"Tupac and Mahalia, - the odd couple meeting kind of early today, eh what? Must be some mighty important dialogue going on today. Me and Little Esther 'bout to go to the breakfast suite, want us to bring you back some victuals to set in the middle of that cute little table of ya'lls?"

Willie Mae Thornton and Little Esther were cut buddies having arrived within the same week in August 1983. Willie Mae died at age 57 of a heart attack and six days later at age 48, Esther Phillips, billed as "Little Esther", died at a medical center where she was being treated for alcoholism and drug abuse. They were two of the most influential blues singers of the Rhythm and Blues era. Big Mama Thornton had influenced and inspired a number of singers including Aretha Franklin, Elvis Presley, and Janis Joplin. Presley's version of Thornton's 1953 hit, "Hound Dog" became one of Presley's biggest pop hits in 1953. Thornton had a close relation to urban blues shouters like Big Joe Turner and Jimmy Rushing. She also played the drums and a mean country blues harmonica.

Little Esther like Big Mama began singing in a Baptist church. As vocalists, they both produced hit records with the Johnny Otis band during the early 1950. Johnny Otis was a white bandleader and his driving big band sounds formed a perfect backdrop for Phillips and Thornton. Esther Phillips was strongly influenced by jazz singer Dinah Washington. She brought popularity to the male/female rhythm and blues duet singing with Mel Walker. Like a lot of musicians on the road, she succumbed to drugs and alcohol.

"Thanks for the invite but no thanks", responded Tupac.

"You ain't the only one there, Tupac, maybe Mahalia might want something. You men folks even up here in the heavens, still think you got to answer for women."

Mahalia joined in, "Big Mama, you right. Just bring me back what they call the continental breakfast, thank you. Oh, and add some sausage and grits to it."

106

"Hailee, that ain't a continental breakfast no more if you add grits and sausage", Little Esther quipped.

"Bring me back some good tasting food that will satisfy my body and soul", said Mahalia turning her attention back to Tupac.

Tupac shrugged lightly and continued, "As I was saying before we were interrupted, the business about a lead singer and choruses and musicians in the background, you can also include the field slaves wherein a leader would start up a song and the others' voices would fall into place, - three and four part harmony and no written notes. That type of call and response is similar to the preacher and his congregation. The call and response becomes musical. So you see what I'm getting at?

The rap artist recites his story or poem accompanied by appropriate background sounds. The griot tells his story and the musical background could be drums. The bard voices heroic themes and the lyre instrument is the background. Leontyne Price sings Puccini and an entire chorus and full orchestra provides the background musical accompaniment. And I could even include Big Mama Thornton because in his seminal study, "Blues People", Amiri Baraka observed that shouters, Jimmy Rushing, Big Joe Turner and Big Mama Thornton, were first heard literally screaming over the crashing rhythm sections and blaring brass sections that were so characteristic of the Southwestern bands. So there you had lead singers and heavy rhythmic background and those singers were telling stories. It's about telling stories that are suitable to populations and generations."

"Tupac, Tupac, Tupac," Mahalia crooned melodiously", now that's where the big differences come in. - Telling the stories. - When singing gospel there is hope in the verses. You may start out weary but you end up with hope based on faith. When blues singers sing the blues, their spirits are down hearted and they stay bogged down hopeless, sad and in misery, yearning for a man and telling how no good the man is and sometimes sin seems to be the only thing that brings them joy. With the blues there seems to be no escaping from the hard, bitter, day today struggles. And then there is the raunchy jazz the Ma Rainey, Bessie Smith jazz/ blues, songs like, "Gimmie a Pig foot", and all that double 'en-tendra' in the songs like, 'I Want a Little Sugar in My Bowl'. Gospel is spiritual and hopeful, not sinful and suggestive."

"You are on the right track, Mom Mahalia, in the sense that people sing, write, talk about their conditions and today's rap singers are doing just that. Shakespeare and Dickens wrote about their times and the social, economic and politics of their time. So be it with the rappers. Mom Mahalia, when they rap about drugs, ho's, guns, bullets, thugs, gangsters, carjacking, killings, murders, - that is their lives. That is their everyday life— run down rotten homes with rats and roaches acting like they own the place, - pimps, shake downs, gang fights, murders, and drug dealers more . common than high school graduates - where's the hope supposed to come from?

Now when I say you could rap, what I mean is you could recite, "Going to Move on Up a Little Higher", with your inimitable soulful voice and add a different rhythmic cadence, an up beat like when you sing "Joshua Fit the Battle of Jericho", well I could provide appropriate background and there you have it, Rapping with Tupac and Mahalia."

"You make it sound so simple and easy but I still have my doubts."

"I am simplifying it. I am not giving you the history of hip-hop music. I haven't even described in detail about the DJ and his scratching on a turntable or diversification in styles, or politicization, - incidentally Grandmaster Flash and the Furious Five released a "message rap", called *The Message* in 1982, and this was one of the earliest examples of recorded hip-hop with a social awareness. And we can't forget the East Coast West Coast rivalry that eventually resulted in the death of yours truly, Tupac Shakur, and the notorious B.I.G. -Senseless murders. -Oh, there are volumes on the story of Rapping and Hip Hop and the term Rap music is sometimes used interchangeably with hip-hop music. This morning, Ma Mahalia, all we are doing is discussing 'gospel rap', as a newcomer to the field of music", explained Tupac.

Mahalia rocked slowly, nodded her head, and with pursed lips, responded, "I think we should include Thomas Dorsey in this discussion. He is known as 'the father of gospel music', yet he started out as a blues pianist, called himself Georgia Tom then and he was truly good. He also played at house rent parties and put together a band called the "Wild Cats Jazz Band", for Ma Rainey, back in the early '20's. Dorsey used to play those raunchy, songs and, now listen to this, Dorsey is called 'the Father of Gospel music' and Ma Rainey is called 'Mother of the Blues'— the blues and gospel, hmm, maybe that's why Thomas Dorsey said that gospel music combines Christian praise with the rhythms of jazz and the blues."

Tupac rose from his seat, clasped his hands, and with a grin as wide as his cheekbones, retorted, "Yes, Mahalia, yes. Now you can see the interconnectedness of music, race, economic conditions and how we, as a people can 'make do'. We struggle through life despite of whatever."

"Son", began Mahalia, "You know I toured with Dorsey for five year at gospel tents and churches. And like me, Thomas Dorsey gave up secular music. Due to personal tragedy, the loss of his wife and first son, - in childbirth – he gave up secular music and began writing and recording what he called "gospel" music. He was the first one to call it gospel. And you know, after his wife's death, Dorsey said that he sat down and the words and melody came to him like spontaneously, - the words and music, "Take My Hand Precious Lord", just came to him, like a revelation. And we all know that's his most famous song and one of the most famous of all gospel songs.

"Don't stop there, Ma Halie", was Tupac's response. "It was a favorite gospel song of the Rev. Martin Luther King, Jr. and by request, *you* sang it at his funeral. Dorsey also wrote 'Peace in the

Valley', especially for you, Mahalia and that too became a gospel standard."

"Oh, yes", reminisced Mahalia, "Precious Lord", has been recorded by so many singers like Elvis Presley, Aretha Franklin, Clara Ward, - now there's another great gospel singer, - and Tennessee Ernie Ford, and even the cowboy, Roy Rogers. And did you know that it was also a favorite of President Lyndon B. Johnson and he too requested that it be sung at his funeral, but he didn't request me."

"Dorsey's father was a minister and his mother a piano teacher. It's clearly recognizable how many of the great musical artists got their start in churches. They either sang in the choir or were musical directors The Black church has produced more than its share of world re-known Black singers of secular music, - blues, pop and jazz and even opera singers. Jessye Norman sang in her church choir and of course, we have the great gospel singers like Shirley Caesar, the Stapleton singers and Albertina Walker, founder of the world- renowned gospel group the Caravans. She later had phenomenal success and was regarded as the "Queen of Gospel." Thomas Dorsey's musical legacy are preserved at Fisk University along with those of W.C. Handy."

"Contrary to what we been saying, Tupac, W.C. Handy didn't get his start in church. As a young child even though he showed a great interest in music and had just an outstanding ear for music, both his family and church frowned upon even the playing of musical instruments. But we know how it is, if the music is in you it will come out in some way or form. You just can't keep the music inside. As a teenager, Handy secretly joined a local blues band and from that time on his musical career grew and grew. He played several instruments, composed music, taught musicians how to read music, - he was a very bright young man, the father of the "blues."

"What W. C. Handy did", said Tupac, "and this is an indication of his genius, was to observe White people's reactions to Black music and he coupled this with his understanding of the Black experience and out of this came his musical compositions called the "blues."

Mahalia began humming under her breath. She possessed a unique booming contralto voice and is known to hum with as much resonance and volume as a normal persons singing voice. She paused and a satisfying smile crossed her lovely, medium chocolate brown face. "I'm thinking about my teenage days when I would listen to Bessie Smith and Ma Rainey. As a result, my gospels became more soulful and energetic. Some of the older church members didn't really appreciate my renditions, thought they were too much like the blues singer. But anytime you talk about music you got to include the blues singers and particularly Bessie Smith and Ma Rainey with their gut bucket, raunchy songs and what I would call, their wild life styles."

Since Tupac's arrival in Revolutionary's Retreat, he spent time reading about the history of black music. Mahalia's words reminded him of a recent reading about female blues singers. He thoughtfully recalled the following:

Bessie Smith, "Empress of the Blues" and Ma Rainey, "Mother of the Blues", are two of the most popular female blues singers who were unique in recording Black women's history and struggles via songs. The topics and words in their songs combined with their personalized and expressive deliveries, created an idiom that has helped black women remember the past and live the present. The glorification of sex and the sexual content of these songs reflects themes and delivers messages about: the nature of and ways to deal with two-timing men; men mistreating women; cheating women; women longing for their men and willing to pay any price to be with their men; men who can't quite measure up sexually and the hardships associated with being, poor, Black women. The titles of the following songs reflect these themes: 'Mean Mistreater Blues", by Memphis Minnie; 'All Fed Up', and 'Ain't No Fool', by Big Mama Thornton; 'Yellow Dog Blues', by Lizzie Miles; 'Tricks Ain't Walkin' No More, by Bessie Jackson' and 'Empty Bed Blues' by Bessie Smith.

The legendary Bessie Smith, the Empress of the Blues, and Ma
Rainey, 'Mother of the Blues' made historical contributions to the
sexual lives of Black women. Michele Russell's "*Slave Codes and
Liner Notes*" made this point succinctly:

> *Bessie Smith redefined our time. In a deliberate inversion
> of the Puritanism of the Protestant ethic, she articulated as
> clearly as anyone did before or since, how fundamental
> sexuality was to survival. Where work was often the death
> of us, sex brought us back to life. It was better than food,
> and sometimes a necessary substitute.*

> *For Bessie Smith, Black women in American culture were
> no longer to be regarded only as sexual objects. She made
> us sexual subjects, the first step in taking control. She
> transformed our collective shame at being rape victims,
> treated like dogs or worse, the meat dogs eat, by
> emphasizing the value of our allure. In so doing, she
> humanized sexuality for Black women.(MR:1982)*

Bessie Smith's songs about house rent parties and buffet flats gave
graphic accounts of entertainment and sex as a necessary part of
economic, spiritual, and emotional survival. House rent parties and
buffet flats were common in Black urban areas offering
entertainments eating, drinking, card playing, gamboling, and sex
was definitely a dominant part of the scene. Ruby Smith, Bessie's
niece by marriage who traveled with her was interviewed by Chris
Albertson, in 1971, and described a buffet flat located in Detroit.

(Interview) RUBY SMITH: ...faggots dressed like women there it
wasn't against the law; you know that Detroit was a *real* open
town for *everybody* in that town. Bessie and us all, went to a party.
Some women there had a buffet flat.
Bessie Smith paid tribute to this establishment in her recording,
"Soft Pedal Blues":
"There's a lady in your neighborhood who runs a buffet flat,
And when she gives a party she knows just where she's at
She gave a dance last Friday night, it was to last 'till one,

112

But when the time was almost up, the fun had just begun."

Albertson: "What's a buffet flat?'
Ruby Smith: A buffet flat is nothing but faggots and, and, uh, bull dykes and open house everything goes on in that house...
Albertson: A gay place?
Ruby Smith: A *very* gay place.
Albertson: Strictly for faggots and bulldykes?
Ruby Smith: Everything! Everything that was in the life, everybody that's in the life...Buffet means everything-_everything goes on. They had a faggot there that was so great people used to come there just to watch him make love to another man. That's right, he was real great, he'd give him a tongue bath and everything. People used to pay good just to see him come there and see him do his act..."*

The mentioning of reefers, bulldykes, sissies, and songs about incestuous relations and copulations were sung without compunction. That was in the '20's and '30's before the current women's liberation and gay activist movements.

Ma Rainey was a featured performer with a troupe in 1912, when Bessie was hired as a dancer rather than a singer. Rainey helped Bessie develop a stage presence and they became friends. At age 16 Ma Rainey heard her first blues song in St Louis, adopted the blues style for her show, and quickly made it her own. She went on to become the top recording artist for Paramount Records. She didn't sign a recording contract until 1923, and that was after 25 years of performing for her many loyal fans. She released over 100 songs in a six-year period including the popular "C. C. Rider", "Bo Weevil Blues", and "Ma Rainey's Black Bottom Blues." Rainey led the transformation of Paramount Records from a subsidiary of a furniture company into a major record label. This is remarkable in consideration of the fact that the period in which Ma Rainey lived, did not provide many opportunities for success for an Afro-American woman living in the Southern United States.

Ma Rainey was bisexual and never denied it. In 1928, she recorded "Prove It On Me" with these lyrics:

"Went out last night with a crowd of my friends,
They must have been women, 'cause I don't like no men.
Wear my clothes just like a fan. Talk to gals just like any old man
'Cause they say I do it, ain't nobody caught me. Sure got to prove it on me."

Mahalia noticing Tupac's reverie interrupted his thoughts. "Tupac, what's on your mind that's got you so thoughtful?"
"Oh, I was just thinking about the role that Black women's music had on the religious, economic, and social realities of Black life and the achievements of these male and female theatrical pioneers. For example, the T.O.B.A. theatre circuit is most likely unknown to Black teenage musical aspirants. The 'Theater Owners Booking Association', commonly called, 'Tough on Black Artists' or Tough on Black Asses, T.O.B.A. was the vaudeville circuit for Blacks performers in the '20's and '30's. The theaters were white owned and collaborated in booking jazz, blues, comedians, and other performers for Black audiences. The association was generally known as Toby Time and booked only Black artists into a series of theaters on the East Coast and as far west as Oklahoma. And let me say that the hardships and the hard knocks that they survived are difficult to fully comprehend today." Tupac looked at Mahalia for consent before continuing.

Mahalia twirled her gold band wedding ring before folding her hands in her lap, tilted her head, and nodded toward her friend.

"Oh, I've heard firsthand about those tours, the months on the road, Jim Crow trains with the colored folks' cars right behind the engines so if you open the windows soot and cinders fly all over you and it was hot in them cars. The bathrooms with no water in the basins or soap - not even toilet paper and you had to carry your own food if you want a decent meal. And those performers were good, you hear me son, they were good, - comedians like Turnip and Butterbeans, they were the best, and the dancers – doing the Cakewalk, Black Bottom, Charleston, time-step and tap dancing. When they were on the road too often they couldn't find a place to stay had to sit up all night in the train station and the same situation with restaurants, no coloreds allowed. That Jim Crow segregation was a mean and hateful business and it was the law."

Tupac continued, "And added to the poor conditions they traveled and worked under, their pay was less than the white performers, and often the theaters didn't pay or paid much less than the agreement called for. The great depression was a great equalizer - the White and Black vaudeville circuits faded. What money was available went for food, not for entertainment on the vaudeville circuit. The T.O.B.A. had many big stars, Ethel Waters, Fats Waller, Duke Ellington, Joe "King" Oliver, Florence Mills, "Pigmeat" Markham, Chick Webb, Josephine Baker and Louis Armstrong to name some.

The most prestigious Black theaters in Harlem, Philadelphia and Washington, D.C. booked acts independently and were not a part of the circuit. The T.O.B.A. was considered less prestigious. Ironically, many Black performers performed in white vaudeville in blackface. To me that's such curious behavior. Segregated theaters and black performers already naturally Black, performing as if they were white and wore black face to make believe they were white. Doesn't make much sense to me."

"Louis Armstrong was a part of that circuit. Now another great musician grew up in poverty in New Orleans, Louisiana, and rose to the top. He started out playing the cornet, then switched to the trumpet and later became a vocalist. He told me that he took to singing because sometimes his lips and tongue and even his teeth were too sore from all the things he did to get those special sounds out of that trumpet. I'll bet you didn't think I knew that much about a jazz- player now did you, Tupac?" concluded Mahalia with a satisfied grin.

"Mahalia, I see you hanging out with those jazz musicians and I hear you humming and crooning right along with them. Now I want to continue our rap discussion, rather our discussion on gospel and rap as co-stars. First, however, I want you to feel comfortable with the arrangement. I know that rap has a history of being profane, sexist, using explicit sexual language, using the "n" word over and over- and just out and out misogynistic. About fifteen years ago, this style of rap generated hundreds of millions of dollars for publicly owned corporations but now rap sales have dropped a dramatic 33% from 2006.

There's this young man, Chamillionaire, who is a platinum-selling rapper and he announced this year that his next album would be cuss-and N-word free. Actually there has always been positive rappers but they haven't received the attention that gangsta rap has." Tupac tapped his stylish brown leather ankle length boots rhythmically as he spoke in cadence, "And you have heard Kirk Franklin", tap, tap, - "and you have heard the musicians, tap-tap – and dancers and songsters" -, tap, tap- "and amidst all that you have gospel" tap- tap.

Mahalia began rocking her body to Tupac's beat and with her soaring alto notes, sang 'amen', a two syllable word into seven syllables, "ay, ay, ay, yay, yay, ay, men", and she held it for what seemed like minutes.
Tupac rose from his chair and gave Mahalia a hug. "Ma Halie, now we got the spirit! Basically I think it would be entertaining and joyful fun for you and me and whoever else listens."

"On that note, Tupac, I'll go along with the creation because that's how I see it, a creation but with certain conditions." Mahalia's smooth brown face broke into an eye squinting unabashed smile.

"Okay, now Ma Hailie, pick out a few of your favorite songs.

"How I Got Over"
"Joshua Fit The Battle Of Jericho"
"In The Upper Room"

116

"Move On Up A Little Higher"

"Now we're ready. We'll call our production, "Rap with Tupac and Ma Jack"

"Tupac, stop! Stop right there! I have a God-given name and I ain't changing it. I can't imagine what goes thru those rapster's heads when they call themselves names like, Puff Daddy, Run DMC, Dr. Dre, Snoop Doggy Dogg and Mos Def, now what kind of names are those? One thing I got to say about your name is that it's legitimate. Your mother, Afeni Shakur, a Black Panther, and I remember that it was in 1972, that she renamed you Tupac Amaru Shakur after an Inca sentenced to death by the Spaniards. In the Inca language, Tupac Amura means shining serpent. But I gotta say that I prefer Tupac to your birth name, Lesane Parish Crooks."

With his signature captivating smile, and speaking from his heart, Tupac softly responded, "Names one gives oneself are important, Ma. The person is trying to tell the world something they feel is important. The world doesn't have to agree but to that individual it's important.

And from all the names of the artists that you mentioned, I want to speak up for Mos Def. He is a brilliant rap artist, a well-respected actor as well and an outspoken critic on social and political issues. He spoke out righteously in the wake of Hurricane Katrina in 2005. He most definitely spoke out when he appeared on the show with Bill Maher. Remember Mahalia? We watched that together, *Real Time with Bill Maher* on September 7, 2007. He stated his belief that Al-Qaeda was not responsible for 9/11, the Apollo Moon landings were a hoax and he spoke about racism against African Americans citing the government response to Hurricane Katrina, the Jena Six and the murder conviction of Mumia Abu-Jamal. Oh, yeah, Mos Def is a force to be reckoned with."

Mahalia muttered halfway to herself, "That's why we're always going to need Gospel to ease the pains and keep having the hope." In a normal tone, she addressed her young friend. "Now I have

117

agreed to begin this venture of gospel rap with you but whether we complete it or not depend on certain agreements. I beamed in on a show recently and they were giving awards to rappers and believe me there was very little that I liked.

All those young men, strutting around the stage with their pants hanging low off their hips, and they repeatedly grabbing at their crotches, but their pants so low that if they grabbed the crotch area they would be grabbing their knees. And holding them black microphones shaped like a penis and the girls, the dancers, my lord, they were moving each limb in a different direction at the same time like a contortionist, - like they were possessed by some spirit but certainly not the holy spirit. And their clothing, what little there was of it, was skintight. I could hardly understand a word they were vocalizing. And I don't know where they got their clothes. All sorts of mixed-matched colors, dark glasses, hats on backwards and sideways and big sneakers! Lord have mercy, I don't know what kind of artists they are. Choreography for the dancers was like high school cheerleaders performing at half time and Tupac, I really can't compare that rhythmic chanting to any kind of a decent singing voice. No, I don't want any part of that kind of rap."

"Mahalia, listen, listen. I would never produce any musical rendition with you without your full permission and would always respect your terms. I understand your perspectives on the rappers you saw, but there are also many positive aspects and performers who do not fit that image you so colorfully described. You set the conditions for the gospel rap and I'll follow.

Here comes Big Mama and Little Esther with your breakfast", said Tupac, as he graciously met the twosome and set the meal on the table.

"Gospel Queen", addressed Little Esther," this morning you have a continental breakfast plus a sampling of down home southern Baptist church breakfast. There's some grits, sausage, gravy and a small slice of hickory-smoked ham."

Big Mama Thornton chimed in, "There's enough there for a hearty meal for one or a regular size meal for two in case you want to share with your handsome buddy with the clean head, , but look here, Big Red and Sistah Sojourner are just about decorating our flagstone paths." The flagstone pathway was designed with the cross strokes of a musical note less than a quarter note.

Greetings were exchanged and after hearing about the gospel rap proposal and declining victuals Malcolm and Sojourner continued their stroll

"I wonder what the future holds for rap and hip-hop", pondered Malcolm.

"Well it all depends on the strength of the controllers."

"What controllers?"

"You know, the capitalists, corporations, and media control of consumers, as well as how the musical historians place it in history. Ain't really about the true value of the music, it's about how it's put out to the public. Rap and hip-hop is saying something about life not in a way that's accepted by what they call mainstream America. The controllers are interested in it for the money they make and that seems to be declining, so no money no more interest. But I don't think it will take a place in musical history like jazz, soul, the blues, and country - western. The way women are portrayed, well, rappers will go down in history as being women haters, what they call it,- mis-sek-ge nation, something like that, as well as making a lot of money for a few."

"Well, one thing I know and that is that many of these young rap and hip-hop artists making millions ought to be in the business of caring for the pioneering musicians who are in dire economic need and never received one tenth of the money these youngsters are making. In my opinion the talent of earlier musicians who are now elderly, is indisputable and those in financial or medical needs

should be cared for. The super rich young ones should develop a plan to provide for their predecessors ", countered Malcolm.
"As we implied earlier in our walk brother, the young, and newly rich need to care about dere fore- runners who made it possible for them to be rich and famous."

"Those elder artists/musicians shouldn't be living in poverty or homes or institutions for the aged and infirmed while these young cats spend literally thousands and thousands of dollars for a two week vacation on a yacht, and own jaguars and Mercedes and homes that are decorated with furniture and objects that they don't even know what they are or what they are for. Homes with swimming pool and half of them can't swim, basketball courts, tennis courts, - all for show, they're seldom used. I think that the majority of the top rappers will be in the Rich and Famous category temporary and unfortunately, many will succumb to alcohol and drugs and get involved with gun warfare. Rap and hip-hop are definitely more than a trend. It has substantive roots and needs to be nurtured so it can take its rightful place in musical history," concluded Malcolm.

The cirrocumulus clouds above the boulevard with their puffy, patchy appearance formed wave like patterns that caught the attention of the pair. They slowed their pace, absorbing the surrounding beauty as they strolled along that marvelous Glory Road Boulevard.

Chapter Six Glossary and Endnotes

- *Amiri Baraka*: Birth name Everett Leroi Jones. He was born in 1934 in Newark, New Jersey and is the author of over 40 books of essays, poems, drama and music. He was the Poet Laureate of New Jersey when America experienced 9-11 terrorism in 2001 and he composed the controversial poem *"Somebody Blew Up America."* He is popularly known for his revolutionary poems and plays.

- *Jimmy Rushing (1903-1972):* Birth name James Andrew Rushing He was an American blues shouter and swing jazz singer from Oklahoma City, Oklahoma. He was a featured vocalist of Count Basie's orchestra from 1935-1948. Rushing was known as *"Mr. Five by Five"*, due to his build. He was a powerful singer with a range from baritone to tenor and could project his voice over the horn and reed section in big bands.

- *Big Joe Turner (1911-1985):* Birth name Joseph Vernon Turner. An American blues shouter from Kansa City, Missouri. He earned his nickname due to his size, 6 feet two inches and 300 plus pounds. He came to his greatest fame in the 1950's with his pioneering rock and roll recordings, particularly, *"Shake, Rattle and Roll."*

- *Jessye Norman:* Born in 1945, in Augusta, Georgia. Norman is a four-time Grammy award winning African-American opera singer. She is one of the most admired contemporary opera singers and recitalists and one of the highest paid performers in classical music. As a performer she is known for her magnetic and dramatic personality and imposing physical presence. She exemplifies the term "diva" with her mannerisms, apparent hauteur and disarming humor.

- *Kirk Franklin:* Born in 1970 in Fort Worth, Texas. He is an African-American gospel music singer and author. He is most notably known as the leader of urban contemporary gospel choirs such as, The Family, God's Property and 1NC (*One Nation Crew*).

- *Interviews with Bessie Smith:* Excerpts from South End Press' 1986 publication of *Common Differences: Conflicts in Black and White Feminist Perspectives*, *Chapter 7: Styling, Profiling & Pretending*- Edited by Gloria I. Joseph & Jill Lewis

Chapter VII

Philosophers and Writers' Retreat

Foreword:

The ideological controversy between W.E B. DuBois and Booker T. Washington has been discussed and popularized by many distinguished, respected, and reputable scholars. It would be a feckless endeavor to attempt to re-examine and further expound on this very complex and historical controversy in this particular book. The Crisis of the Negro Intellectual by Harold Cruse, published by William Morrow & Company, Inc. (1967) and Crisis of the Black Intellectual by W. D. Wright published by Third World Press (2007) are two recommendations that provides well substantiated material with deft explanations concerning the political, economic and racial ideological differences and similarities between Washington and DuBois.

The opinions of writers that are either defenders or supporters of DuBois or Washington are at times fierce and contentious, belittling and praising, condemning and promoting attitudes, character, and deeds of both men. These opinions are insightful, thought provoking, and reveal the shortcomings of ideologue worship.

The inclusion of Marcus Garvey, a disciple of Washington, is a welcomed participant in the discourse. Harold Cruse crystallizes this importance in these words, "Out of this amazing historic, triangular feud came everything of intellectual, spiritual, cultural, and political value to the American Negro. Even today, the views of Washington vs. DuBois vs. Garvey are still debated…" From Crisis of the Black Intellectual—pg. 334

As the complex of "Philosophers and Writers Retreat" came in to view, Sojourner noticed a particularly lofty cloud vibrating energetically over one of the cabins. Hearing familiar voices cavorting through the air she mused, "Looks like even the clouds reflecting and reacting to that ongoing conversation between dose two."

Malcolm shook his head ruefully as the intensity and erudition of the debaters' arguments ricochet through the air.

"Higher education is a MUST for Blacks. We must become equally skilled in the arts, and humanities, philosophy, literature, political science, economics, medicine and languages, languages, languages."

With hands clasped before him, Booker T. Washington leaned forward in the hand carved oak rocker and responded, "Look how our people are still unemployed. The latest figures for unemployment among our youth are way above the national level for whites. Education levels for Blacks also way below the national levels and dropout rates, the dropout rates are far above the national level. Now how uplifting is that for our people? I beg the question, how uplifting is that for our people? Recall Dr. DuBois, in my industry, my teaching, we kept three things in mind: To learn to do things that the world wants done; to graduate from the school with enough skills coupled with intelligence and moral character to enable them to make a living for themselves and others; and to know that labor is dignified and beautiful."

"Brother Washington, how can we prepare our people to serve a human kind that is morally bankrupt? Yes, labor could and should be dignified, but how can it be when you have farmers, share croppers, migrant workers, domestics, sweatshop workers, continuously being exploited, working under wretched, unhealthy, degrading conditions and being underpaid all at the same time. America has never allowed Blacks to be full citizens, to be treated as full citizens and it has never allowed women to be full citizens. And even if Blacks acquired and practiced all the skills possible, it would not change America's foundation of inequality."

Philosophers and Writers Retreat consisted of a group of majestically hewn log cabins with spacious verandas. The grounds separating each house were covered with river stones interspaced with polished agates. Several pools were scattered around the grounds, some containing brilliant colored carps and others with varieties of water lilies, and all with fountains bubbling and

124

gurgling melodiously. Guests entering Dubois' cabin were immediately captured by 24 x 12 inch portraits of women he honored. His deep respect and appreciation for women is clearly shown in a paragraph from his book, Darkwater Voices from Within the Veil.

"I shall forgive the white South much in its final judgment day: I shall forgive its slavery, for slavery is a world-old habit; I shall forgive its fighting for a well-lost cause, and for remembering that struggle with tender tears; I shall forgive its so-called "pride of race," the passion of its hot blood, and even its dear old, laughable, strutting and posing; but one thing I shall never forgive, neither in this world nor the world to come; its wanton and continued and persistent insulting of the black womanhood which it sought and seeks to prostitute to its lust. I cannot forget that it is such Southern gentlemen into whose hands smug Northern hypocrites of today are seeking to place our women's eternal destiny, men who insist upon withholding from my mother and my wife and daughter those signs and appellations of courtesy and respect which elsewhere he withholds only from bawds and courtesans." (Chapter VII The Damnation of Women, page 172)

On the wall facing north, in black walnut frames were the portraits of strong women of spiritual ancestry: Lillian Ngoyi and Harriet Tubman. Accompanying them, in silver frames on the adjoining wall were photos of Mary Fields and Phyllis Wheatley. Adjacent to each portrait was a biographical script that Dr. Dubois had personally approved. A consummate researcher, it gave him great satisfaction to obtain material about Phyllis Wheatley from a collector's item book, LIGHT AND TRUTH, written in 1884. *

Lillian Ngoyi 1911 – 1980—*South African anti-apartheid activist. In 1952, she joined the ANC Women's League and in 1953, she was elected President of the Women's League.*

On August 9, 1956, "Ma Ngoyi", as she was affectionately called, led a march along with Helen Joseph, Albertina Sisulu and Sophia Williams De Bruyn of 20,000 women to the Union Building of Pretoria in the celebrated passbook protest. The apartheid government required that women carry passbooks as part of the pass laws. Ngoyi was a strong orator and an inspiration to her colleagues in the ANC. She was arrested in 1956, spent 71 days in solitary confinement and 11 years under severe bans and restrictions that often confined her to her home in Orlando, Soweto. A community health Center in Soweto is named in her honor. On August 9, 2006, the 50th anniversary of the march on Pretoria, Strijdom Square from which the women marched, was renamed Lillian Ngoyi Square and August 9th is now commemorated in South Africa as Women's Day. Lillian Ngoyi was resilient, fortuitous and a stalwarts of the anti-apartheid struggles. She was the first woman elected to the executive committee . of the African National Congress and helped launch the Federation of South African Women.

Harriet Tubman 1820 – 1913— *Born a slave of pure African ancestry in Maryland she was one of the most important agents of the Underground Railroad and leader of fugitive slaves. Year after year, she penetrated the slave states and personally led over 300 slaves north without losing a single one. She was called "the Moses of her people." A $10,000 standing reward was offered for her capture but she said, 'The whites can't catch us, for I was born with the charm, and the Lord has given me the power." Auburn, New York was the base of her operations where a number of sympathetic Quakers were central to the Underground Railroad operations. She was closely associated with the Abolitionist John Brown and missed the raid on Harper's Ferry due to illness. She reportedly suffered from narcolepsy because of a severe blow to her head at age 12, inflicted by a white overseer because she refused to assist in tying up a man who had attempted to* escape. At the outbreak of the Civil War Harriet Tubman served as a soldier, spy, and nurse. After the close of the Civil War Harriet Tubman returned to Auburn where she helped Auburn become a center of activity in support of women's rights. She built a wooden structure for her home that later became a home for the aged and indigent. After her death she was buried in Fort Hill Cemetery in Auburn with military honors. In 1995, the federal government honored Harriet Tubman with a commemorative stamp bearing her name and likeness.

Mary Fields 1832 – 1914—A robust, six feet, 200-pound African-American female pioneer of the West, was aka, Black Mary. She lived a tough, high-spirited life, like a female Paul Bunyan. – 'If you see her coming better step aside'. She hauled freight and did heavy chores, driving eight horses pulling two wagons. At age 50, Mary Fields was the second woman to drive a U.S. Mail coach and in those days that meant you had to be prepared for robbers and thieves as you protected the mail and passengers. She epitomized the Wild West characterization of a tough hombre. She is described as always toting a rifle and pistol, a cigar clenched in her teeth and a jug of whiskey nearby. Legend has it that she single handedly fought off a pack of wolves, and would fight with any man who insulted her. She is also reputed to have been an astute entrepreneur having owned a restaurant and operated an under- cover money- lending - business. Fact vs. legend is intertwined but we know that Mary Fields was symbolic of the pioneering, courageous, cunning female who was central to the making of the West.

Phyllis Wheatley 1753 – 1784—At the age of seven or eight years in 1761, Phyllis, a slave, was brought from Africa to America and sold to Mr. John Wheatley. She lived with his family, respectful citizens of Boston, Massachusetts. They provided home schooling and her academic progress particularly in the areas of reading and *writing were indications of her African genius. Phyllis rapidly learned the English language, studied Latin, and began writing poetry. Encouraged to publish her poems she did so and in 1767, became the first Black woman to publish a poem. Three years later, she became the first Black woman to publish a book. In 1773, she published a volume of poetry. From her writings, it is evident that she had done extensive reading for she often alludes to the classic writers of antiquity, which shows that she was familiar with their works. She died in 1784, at the tender year of about 31, leaving behind a history of outstanding achievements.*

The voices came from within the living room of one of the Retreat's most highly revered inhabitants, W.E.B DuBois. It was in his celestial quarters that the scholars, educators, philosophers, poets and writers met to dialogue about the planet earth its inhabitants and its social, political, economic, and environmental influences worldwide.

Elegant and stylish as always, in a three-piece lightweight grey pin striped suit, pearl studs, and a light blue striped cravat, Dr. DuBois studied his guest and carefully selected his words as he continued their conversation.

"Mr. Washington, I met you in this firmament in August, 1963, forty eight years after your arrival in 1915, and since that time we have had many discussions about our individual philosophies of life, our political postures and what was/is best for the Negro, now referred to as Black, African American, or Afro-American. And it has become very clear to me and I always maintained, that the study of the progress and mistreatment of Blacks should not be limited to the states but to the Black Diaspora. That is the proper way to consider the questions due to ancestral relationship and the collective consciousness of Black folk.

At this time, it behooves us to enlighten the public on our current views about America's social and religious policies. Time and time again, from the mouths of people from every class, color, and religion, our differences have been defined in mind-blowing simplicity. Our statesmanship, our contributions to society and philosophies of education are disregarded and we are defined in the following ridiculously simple terms: - Booker T. Washington the accommodator for white people and W.E.B. Dubois, believer in a talented ten for black progress.   This   debilitating   misunderstanding and shortsighted misrepresentations of the two of us needs to be remedied. Here's my suggestion, Dr. Washington, let us tell the people, in our own words how our history affects today's generation. Or in other words what bearings do our past deeds and accomplishments have on the lives of Blacks today."

"Add a cup of ginger tea from IDA'S PLACE, to that idea and I'm ready to begin", Washington responded.

W.E.B. Dubois prepared the beverage and laid the Wedgwood cups and saucers on his well-polished English mahogany two-leaf table.

"Would you like some biscuits as well?" ask DuBois.

"Yes, to the biscuits but I prefer my tea in a mug. The best tasting tea is drunk from earthenware mugs. From the potter's wheel, to the kiln, to the table, to me," cajoled Booker T.

The tea and biscuits were served in accordance with his guest's satisfaction. DuBois preferred his Wedgwood and one of Ida's corn muffins. Settled in their comfort zones, Washington and DuBois began doing what history books rarely do, that is capture the true essence of events and true character of prestigious persons.

Booker T. Washington started the discussion. "I'd like to begin by talking about my childhood as it is. I advise all persons if they haven't already, read this book, <u>Up From Slavery</u>, and educate your self. I was born a slave in 1856. My mother was a Black cook, and my father was a white man, from a neighboring farm so I was what was called a mulatto. That means an offspring of mixed parentage, one parent Black and the other white. Rape was a form of life on the plantations. It was a common practice throughout slavery for southern white plantation owners to have their way with any Black woman of their choice.

In those days, the offspring of whites and blacks were not called bi-racial. Oh, no, we were more likely called hybrids, mutts, or mongrels and if whites mated with Indians, their offspring were called half-breeds or mixed breed. There was no glamour whatsoever affiliated with being a mulatto, except I should say for those mulatto young ladies who became mistresses. If anything, a mulatto was associated with being an animal, - mongrels. As handsome, strapping and brilliant as Frederick Douglass was, he too was a mulatto slave and received the harsh and cruel punishment given to slaves, but he fought through it all, rose above it all and became a fearless champion for civil rights.

Nowadays we see super stars like Halle Berry, Mariah Carey, James Blake, Derek Jeter, and Tony Parker, to name several, called bi-racial. And we can't leave out that presidential hopeful, Barack Obama. They are celebrities, rich and good-looking, - that is according to America's definition of good looking, that is based on the closer your features and skin color are to whites the more likely you are considered good-looking. Of course, the big difference is that their parents had a choice. They are not the product of rapes. However, all the bi-racial-ites should know the history of miscegenation and the unscientific categorizing of races. Let us look at the way Whites determined who was white and who was not. One drop of Black blood and you were no longer considered white. You had black folks "passing" for whites then and now. Now if one drop of black blood made you a non-white, why not one droplet of white blood making you a non-black? Why was all that power given to one drop of Black blood?

The very term 'mulatto', just what does that mean? The word denoting a person of mixed Black and White heritage is Spanish in origin and means nothing more than 'hybrid' but because of its association with slavery, has a derogatory implication. The word 'mule' is similarly derived from the Spanish for 'hybrid', and came to serve as a metaphor for a cross between the refined White plantation owner (thoroughbred horse) and the lowly, inferior Black slave (*donkey*). Whites associated us with animals and chattel, but they were also fearful of our resilience our ability to endure their beastly treatment. And that White man's promise of "40 acres and a mule" was a cruel joke because a mule is a cross between a donkey and a horse and it's sterile, and you know for sure that mulattoes are not sterile."

"Brother Washington, with all due respect, if you continue with your digressions, as interesting and truthful as they may be, your narrative will continue throughout the entire day. But let me add, color caste, a legacy of miscegenation operates today with its tentacles more devastating within Black communities than it did in slave communities. Race as we should all know by now, has no scientific definition, it is a social construct designed to classify people with the desired outcome of establishing hierarchies that always results in gradations of superior and inferior categories. This of course establishes a pecking order based on what skin color you possess.

I was born in 1868, in the town of Great Barrington, Massachusetts. My father was a descendant of French Huguenots and my mother came from a long line of Black Burghardts that moved in and out around the color line. According to the ersatz race categories I would be called, - not mulatto, not quadroon, but probably an octoroon. As a child, I did not suffer the cruel physical hardships that were a part of daily plantation life. Now that is not to say that I did not experience racism. Any Black American who uses that phrase, 'I never experienced racism' **is either ignorant beyond belief, illusionary or suffering from the most severe case of denial imaginable.** Today I believe my use of the term "double consciousness" is extremely apt among the bi-racial youth."

Mr. Washington typically dressed formally and today was no exception. He fingered his black bow tie and the collar of his white starched shirt, whose cuffs slightly showed below the sleeves of his brown suit jacket, and acknowledged his host.

"You are quite correct but history cannot be linear and today's youth have too little knowledge about the past, so forgive me for my brief digressions. Your digression Brother DuBois impels me to elaborate on your term double consciousness. In <u>Souls of Black Folks,</u> you eloquently spoke *of '...the African American's sense of two-ness – of un-reconciled strivings of being an American, A Negro: two souls two thoughts...two warring ideals in one dark body. The divided self merges with the other racial selves and in this merging the African-American wishes neither of the older selves to be lost. He would not Africanize America, for America has too much to teach the world and Africa. He would not bleach his Negro soul in a flood of White Americanism for he knows that Negro Blood has a message for the world.'*

DuBois continued this line of thought. "The bi-racial youth complicate the problem. The double consciousness applies to the African-American, two souls in one dark body, Africa and Americanization. With the bi-racial, the two souls have become one. So there is one mixed soul in one beige body. The African American part has already been compromised –the warring souls are integrated. The Negro soul has been bleached, the white part, whether it be American, French, German, Chinese, Korean, has been adulterated – no longer 'pure'. There is a new self, the biracial self. The older soul, the older self, the dark-skinned American becomes lost when the category, bi-racial becomes an acceptable racial definition. Unfortunately, bi-racials do not have full acceptance in either of the ersatz Black or White races. Hence, the bi or multi-racial category becomes a holding ground while society finds a profitable way to utilize this particular category."

"Dr. DuBois, you do have a way of introducing new thought processes to the world. Let the bi-racials rest a bit while I continue my narrative. My early life was a typical slave life. Hard work at an early age, all the basics necessary for decent living denied, even communication among us curtailed and many of us suffered the cruel, inhumane tortures, the beatings, whippings and the ultimate so-called punishments, - the lynching.

That brings me to the point of wanting to discuss the current Jena 6 case. Last year in August 2006, in Jena, Louisiana, white high school students hung nooses in a tree to communicate antipathy toward their African-American classmates. A black student had sat under a tree known as a gathering spot for white students. Three white students later hung noses from the tree. That led to outbreaks of fighting between blacks and whites. The District Attorney prosecuted the six Black teenagers involved in the fights while the white noose hangers received brief suspensions. That led to a huge protest, in September, 2007, with over 50,000 people converging on the little town of Jena, with 3,500, regular residents."

Mr. Washington smoothed down his reddish gray hair with worked- worn hands, relishing in his story telling. "I know I'm digressing but these incidents are important in the sense that they show how much history repeats itself and the need for constant vigilance to protect your rights. Let me talk about the history of the rope. Many young folks do not even know what the word lynching means and if they do not know the meaning, they do not know their history. Lynching, hangings became a routine practice in the country."

"Lynching", Dr. DuBois involuntarily shuddered as he said the word. It brought to mind memories, horrifying memories. Eyes half closed behind his steel framed glasses he mused, *'It is 2007, and one of the darkest chapters, one of the most ugly, violent episodes in America, the violence committed against Negro citizens by Whites, the history of lynching - remains a pocket of ignorance, a blithe historical ignorance'*

DuBois regained his composure; gently stroked his trimmed goatee and said, "In hearing classroom discussions, reading articles and viewing T.V. and other media via the time gazer, it is clear that lynching is a foreign word to many Americans. The truth of the matter is, and here I quote from the research of Robert A. Gibson,

'Lynching, - open public murders of individuals suspect of crime conceived and carried out more or less spontaneously by a mob- seem to have been an *American invention** In the last decades of the nineteenth century, the lynching of Black people became an institutionalized method used by Whites to terrorize Blacks and maintain white supremacy.'"

Washington interrupted, "Most lynching were by hanging, however, many were of a more hideous nature- the burning at the stake, maiming, dismemberment, castration. Oh, I remember it well. In 1892, the largest number of lynchings occurred that year. I believe 230 persons were lynched, 161 Blacks, and sixty-nine whites. It was a cruel combination of racism and sadism. Lynching became a sort of recreation. Mobs would gather consisting of families with their young children to witness a lynching. And they even handed out dismembered body parts to their children as souvenirs! Now how barbaric can one get!" Dr. Washington shook his head in renewed indignation and disgust.

"The most common practice was the hanging with the noose. That is when a rope with a slipknot is placed around the neck of the individual and the end of the rope tied to a branch of a tree. The CRISIS, the official organ of the NAACP of which you, DuBois, was editor, kept independent records and statistics on lynching. Lynching was not a crime exclusively committed against Blacks. White men and women were victims but their numbers were very, very, significantly smaller."

More memories crowded DuBois. He thought of a conversation he recently had with Frederick Douglas wherein Douglas retold this story:

'One day at home in 1890, I received a visit from Mary Church Terrell, at the time a young schoolteacher, and she told me a friend was killed. 'Lynched, Mr. Douglas, lynched.' Her lips twitched with grief and anger.

I knew the meaning of the word: torture, hanging, burning at the stake, the mutilation of a lifeless body. Negroes could be lynched for anything in the South-for insulting a White person, for turning down a poorly paid job, for being unpopular, for complaining about being cheated. I went to see President Harrison who listened and said little and did less. But I still raised my voice in public protest not only against the crimes of the lynch mobs, but against the "who cares" attitude of the whole country. The men who break open jails with bloody hands destroy human life are not alone responsible. They simply obey the public sentiment of the South-the sentiment created by wealth and respectability, by the press and the pulpit'."

Memories, memories. This time DuBois thought of Billy Holiday and the song, "*Strange Fruit*"*

> "*Southern trees bear a strange fruit,*
> *Blood on the leaves and blood at the root,*
> *Back bodies swaying in the Southern breeze,*
> *Strange fruit hanging from the poplar trees..*
> *Pastoral scene of the gallant South,*
> *The bulging eyes and the twisted mouth,*
> *Scent of magnolia sweet and fresh,*
> *Then the sudden smell of burning flesh.*
> *Here is a fruit for the crows to pluck,*
> *For the rain to gather, for the wind to suck,*
> *For the sun to rot, for the trees to drop,*
> *Here is a strange and bitter fruit.*"

DuBois thought of Rufus Moncrief who in 1917 was beaten senseless by a mob that then used a saw to cut off his arms. The mob hanged Moncrief and then hanged his dog for good measure.

DuBois thought of Luther Hulbert and his wife who in 1904 had their fingers chopped off and handed out as souvenirs. Hulbert was beaten so badly one of his eyes came out. It hung by a thread. A large corkscrew bored into the couple's flesh. Rope was used to tie them to the tree.

DuBois thought of Mary Turner. In 1918, she was burned alive in Valdosta, Georgia. A man used a hog-splitting knife to slash her swollen stomach. The baby she had carried nearly to full term tumbled out and managed two cries before the man crushed its' head beneath his heels. A rope was used to tie Mary Turner upside down in a tree. (*"History of Rope"**)

And he finally thought of Ida Wells Barnett and her relentless crusade against lynching. How in 1892, she published her pamphlet, <u>Southern Horrors: Lynch Law in All Its Phases.</u> This documented her research and campaign against lynching. After examining many accounts of lynching based on alleged "rape of white women", she concluded that Southerners concocted the rape excuse to hide the real reason for lynching black men: Black economic progress, which threatened not only white Southerners pocketbooks but also their ideas about black inferiority.

Silence. A motionless silence came over the room. The souls of lynched Black folks. The bubbling of the fountains in the gardens became a muffled laborious gurgle. Both men, DuBois and Washington, were in repose, - their bodies emitting shards of light. Incredibly, the four photos of the women on the wall became three-dimensional. Holograms!

Several moments later DuBois turned toward Booker T. and murmured, "Lynching was a means of social control. Since those times there have been changes but when we read about Jena, Louisiana and beam in on a young woman including in her Halloween outdoor home decorations, a figure with a dark face hanging from a noose, we know that racism is on the rise and it is largely due to a lack of education and, as Frederick Douglass put it, the "who cares" attitude of the whole country. This part of American history, lynching, must be a part of all school curriculums."

Washington responded, "Getting back to my past, and speaking of schools, I say, with tongue in cheek, that as a young boy I went to school, but not as a student. I carried books for one of the plantation owner's daughters. It was illegal to educate slaves but

136

we know about the concept of latent learning. In addition we learned by osmosis, imitation, pretending not to know and attending clandestine schools.

After the Emancipation Proclamation in 1865, I was nine, my family moved to West Virginia and my life as a laborer began in earnest. Worked in the salt mines, worked as a houseboy and my learning increased due to the kindness of the master's wife. At age 16, I traveled back to Virginia and enrolled in Hampton Institute. It was a 500-mile journey and I walked most of the way. I can honestly say that there was no period in my life devoted to play. Almost every day of my life was occupied by some form of labor."

"Booker, you definitely deserve to rest and relax and enjoy the unhurried atmosphere in Revolutionary's Retreat. You became an instructor at Hampton and then founded Tuskegee Institute in 1881. You founded it, nurtured it, and developed the "Tuskegee Machine." Let the American public know the enormity of you and your leadership. Undeniably, there was a great ideological controversy between us, which later became more personal and bitter than I had ever dreamed.

Nonetheless it must be recognized that from 1895 when you made your famous "Atlanta Compromise" speech, until 1919, you Booker T., were the most powerful Black man in America. You were essentially the leader of both the Black and White races. Power, status, and prestige brother, you had it all. And while I still have the floor, let me say that while it is thought that Marcus Garvey established the first mass movement among Blacks in the United States, your mass movement involved millions and reached a magnitude and quality of adulation, affection, loyalty, and devotion that Garvey never could have attained in America."

"Yes, I had the Tuskegee Machine" but you had a solid hold at Atlanta University and produced a masterpiece, <u>Black Reconstruction</u> that dealt with the socio-economic development of the nation after the Civil War. You emphasized the contributions of Blacks people to this period when previously we were portrayed as disorganized and chaotic."

"I appreciate the compliment but I never had the following of the masses as you did, and again I quote from W. D. Wright's <u>Crisis of the Black Intellectual</u>."

"Washington had a hold on rural Blacks in the South and also had a hold over Blacks in the North. In both places, he always spoke to over flowing crowds with hundreds of thousands of people standing outside of building to see him when he came in and when he left. In the South they flocked by the thousands to see him or hear him speak, coming from miles around, leaving work and everything else behind to do so. Washington had a hold on rural Blacks but also southern and northern urban Blacks, with the southern rural Blacks making up the mass movement that he had initiated in the 1880's. This hold propelled him to Atlanta in 1895 and under his general leadership for the remainder of his life." (*Wright, pg.202*)

"Now that's mighty generous of you Dr. DuBois. You lost some of your haughtiness since you been here", Washington said with a sparkle in his grey eyes. "Too many of the 21 century critics of my philosophies suffer from the "zeitgeist." They measure my actions against the social and political scenes of today, and do not realize that I changed with the times. My policies of accommodation in the 1800's were no different from the ongoing every day accommodations that Black people had to do in the late nineteenth and early twentieth century. Accommodating White people, their racism and their racist power and practices was just something that Black people had to do. I merely claimed the practice and tried to make it work in some way for the benefit of our people. At that time I sincerely believed that Black people should concentrate their energies on industrial education."

By now the tea, biscuits, and corn muffins had all but disappeared except for a few crumbs that were displaced as the men were making their pronouncements. Dr. DuBois rose up to replenish the refreshments in preparation for the remarks that were bubbling to make themselves heard.

"As the saying goes," began DuBois as he carefully poured the tea, "out of every bad comes something good and in the summer of 1903, when you addressed a rally in Boston, you were verbally assaulted by Monroe Trotter and he was jailed on trumped-up charges and I know you recall, Brother Washington, how very upset I became."
Between swallows of his ginger tea Washington gingerly injected, "Yes, and I know you and others thought that I was behind those charges. It's too long ago for me to remember precisely what happened but I do recall and from good sources that you were ready to start a revolution."

"And in a sense that's exactly what happened. That incident prompted me to organize a group, you can call them revolutionaries if you wish, but I was looking for men who would aggressively fight for the full freedom and the economic, political, cultural, and educational growth for Blacks. This led to the organization of twenty-nine men and the establishment of the Niagara Movement so called because the meeting was held on the Canadian side of Niagara Falls, since we were prevented from meeting on the U.S. side. Our primary purpose was to advocate civil justice and abolish caste discrimination. We did not succeed but we merged with some white liberals and the National Association for the Advancement of Colored People was formed. Yes, the NAACP was born out of frustration and previous failed attempt of organization, and it is still going strong today."

With a mischievous grin Washington commented, "Well, the way I see it Dr. DuBois, I should receive credit for the establishment of the NAACP and also for the CRISIS magazine for which you were the editor-in-chief for 25 years"

"I see you haven't loss your ability to turn a disadvantage to your advantage, but you always were a good con man, leading both Blacks and Whites and making each group feel like they were getting the best of the deal." DuBois' eyes twinkled as he suppressed a smile.

"As my memory tells me, when it comes to acumen you have little or no peers. Through The CRISIS -news and policies concerning the NAACP- were distributed and you as editor-in-chief projected that which you felt the public needed to know. Now that's pretty crafty."

"You will get no argument from me on that score, Booker T.; I definitely used the CRISIS as a vehicle for revealing America's bigotry and the racism, the lawful lynching and the disgraceful treatment of Black veterans that fought heroically in the World War I." DuBois was searching for additional muffins as he grumbled. "Now why didn't I order more of Ida's blue berry muffins? Just talking about my efforts to convince the country that legal action should be taken against lynching requires stamina and those muffins could do just that."

"It was also around that time that you encountered the honorable Marcus Garvey and the Universal Negro Improvement Association (UNIA) designed for the purpose of uniting Africa and her descendants. In a typical DuBois style you described the man as 'a hard working idealist, but his methods are bombastic, illogical and almost illegal and you also called him some ugly names including the word 'ugly'", said Booker.

DuBois turned his head around sharply, his light bluish eyes glimmering with indignation. "Now this was to be a civil discussion. You have changed throughout your life and so have I. It is progressive to mature."

"As I was saying in defense of Garvey he like you, had mass support and tremendous appeal. Oh, he was triumphant, - had thousands chanting his phrase, "Up you mighty people. You can accomplish what you will." He held pageants and parades through Harlem with red, black and green liberation flags as he tried to

carry out his visionary concept of buying ships for overseas trade and travel,- to get Black people to become economically viable.'
"How different was his vision of having Blacks become leaders, self-sufficient and make forward progress from your vision and from my vision? Didn't all three of us strive for the betterment of our people?"

DuBois, edged forward on his rocker, aimed steely eyes on Washington's smooth, beige countenance worn beyond his 59 years and spoke, "Marcus Garvey had a philosophy of Black consciousness, self-help, and economic independence. You had a philosophy of commitment to industrial labor, intra- Black economic self-sufficiency and high moral and religious development. What both of your ideologies lacked were a sound economic theory and there was a profound neglect of the influences or even the mere existence of capitalism and imperialism. Yes, there was definitely some commonality in our goals, we all strived for the improvement the betterment of our people, but there were tremendous differences in our methods of attaining these goals. There were also considerable differences in our legions of support."

Booker T. did not immediately respond to DuBois, rather he focused on the photo of the comely face of Lillian Ngoyi. As he glanced away, he recognized another distinctive woman of African ancestry, majestically swinging her walking stick, crossing the pebbled grounds of Writer's Retreat. Closely following was Malik El Shabazz.

"Looks like we may be having some company, Dr. DuBois I'll wager these two can add some contemplative thoughts on the subject."

Dr. DuBois rose and politely addressed and invited the duo into his elegantly furnished living room.

"Much obliged to be here. Down the road, apiece there were many fireworks in the air, but as we came closer, I was relieved to hear friendly banter. However, we won't be staying' long. We intend to finish our stroll before sunrise turn to sunglow. Our main reason for stopping' was to bring you these tasty coconut blueberry muffins from Ida. She asked us to drop them off knowing how much you enjoy them."

"Dr. DuBois", grinned Malcolm, "what she actually said was, 'Please deliver these meticulously baked, scrumptious delicacies to Dr. DuBois. I am astutely aware of his gratuitous appreciation of culinary perfection.'"

Joyfully, Dubois told Malcolm, "However or whatever she said, I am quite thankful. I was just saying that I needed more energy to continue our discussion and now I will be well fortified."

Mr. Washington explained to the twosome, "We were discussing what effect our earthly deeds and actions have on today's generations. Now DuBois was key to the establishment of the NAACP and the publication of the CRISIS magazine and just looka here, 2007, and the NAACP still going strong and trying to recruit younger members and the CRISIS magazine still printing the most accurate and critical articles that Blacks need to know about. My philosophy of learning useful vocational skills, having strong moral character, appreciating the value of education, could serve our youth well if they practiced them."

DuBois countered, "How can they practice what they were never taught? You cannot practice what you do not know. To what extent is youth of today familiar with what we accomplished? Do they even KNOW what we accomplished? How aware are they of civil rights struggles? What does Pan Africanism mean to them? Do they realize why they should be concerned about the atrocities in Darfur, in the Sudan?"

"Earlier you were saying Brother Washington, about slaves breaking the laws and risking beatings to learn to read and today with all the high tech reading methods, year after year young Blacks exit schools as functional illiterates, Of course, I'm familiar with progress reports concerning the number of Black college graduates and the two or three CEO's or the increased numbers on the corporate level, but we are talking about the overall conditions of Blacks, - the numbers living below the poverty level, the inordinate high number in jails, the high homicide rate among Blacks, inadequate health care, the gross injustice in the justice systems."

Rising up from his chair and gesturing, his arms muscular from a life- time of hard manual labor, Washington delivered, "Schooling, schooling is important today as it was during my youth. All students, Black and White should be familiar with the Little Rock Nine. Some youngsters probably think the Little Rock Nine, was a rock group or a rap song. Fifty years ago, in the spring of 1957, nine brave Black students tried to enter the Central High School in Little Rock, Arkansas, the state capital. As the students tried to enter the Arkansas National Guard, called out by the governor, Orval Faubus stopped them to 'protect the citizens of Little Rock'. Those nine youth became heroes as they endured the racial hatred of hostile, ignorant, vicious, stupid white mobs. Those nine students paved the way for equal education, for desegregated schools. It wasn't the simple stroke of a pen that enabled the legal opportunity for a decent education for today's Black students. The actions of those in the past accounts for the rights we have today, rights that will erode if we do not remain vigilant."

"It was Daisy Bates- *remember her name, along with the other great women freedom fighters*- who as president of the Arkansas NAACP, called upon attorney Thurgood Marshall- *remember his name too, he was the first Black Supreme Court Judge*- to deal with the legal aspects of the case. Although not in school, the Little Rock 9 continued their studies at home. Three weeks after their first attempt to enter the school the National Guard was removed and a small contingent of police officers escorted those students into the school. Even with police escorts, a vicious mob overran the police and threatened the lives of the students. The nine students were taken from the school and driven to safety as a riot erupted on the school grounds. The mob threw bricks, smashed

143

school windows, broke doors, and beat reporters. Can you imagine that, grown White people going to that length to prevent nine young Blacks from entering a school. The actions of the Little Rock Nine, is a part of history that MUST NOT be forgotten."

"At the start of the 20th century I predicted that the problem of the 20th century would be the problem of the color-line and in 1903 I wrote about the permanence of the racial problem and the absence of true democracy in America. Today, in the year 2007, the 21st century, where are we in terms of racial problems and equality for all? None can deny the changes in our lives with regard to laws against desegregation and discrimination in employment, schooling and housing and even marriage. There are more appointed Black officials and college students organizing for more than homecoming queens and fraternity hazing. Beamed in on the Tom Joyner show last week and heard about college students involved in fund raising to increase the number of incoming freshmen. On the other hand, none can deny the daily racial injustices from racial profiling to 19th century style lynching. Just last year a Black man was tied to a truck and dragged to his death."

"Today's generations must become cognizant of the facts that generations before them were trailblazers. The easy entry that today's generation has in to restaurants, hotels and movie houses did not happen due to the good will of corporate America."

"Truer words were never spoken, Dr. DuBois", interjected Malcolm, "but please do not let us interrupt this dialogue. As Sister Sojourner said, we must be on our way." Adieus were said all around and Malcolm and Sojourner continued on their way.

Several paces down the air-paved skyway, Malcolm began, "Those two are quite a pair. One arrived at age 59, after practically working his self to death, and the other arrived at 95, after becoming a citizen of Ghana. Think there's something special about that reversal of numbers?"

144

"It's about numerology and there is always something meaningful when it comes to numbers. Numbers plagued 'em and made them prosperous all their lives. Those numbers show they had more similarities than differences."

"In my estimation, Sojourner, William Edward Burghardt DuBois, is one of the most prophetic, prolific, Pan Africanists I ever met. The man is a genius. He is by nature, intellectually gifted. Graduated from Fisk College and entered Harvard University classified as a junior. That means four years at a Black College was equal to two years at a White college, -ain't that something! After Harvard, he studied two years at the University of Berlin, in Germany. It was during that time that he began to see the race problems in the Americas, Africa and Asia and the political development of Europe as one. It was also during this time that his studies of history, economics, and politics were united into a scientific approach of social research."

"I reckon it was also the beginning of his Pan African- ism, so they call it. I never left' America but ", and here Sojourner gave one of her wisdom-filled chuckles, "Africa never left me. Every slave and ancestors of slaves knows that Africa is where they come from and where you come from is your home and everybody should be concerned 'bout their home and family."

"Well said, Sister. Brother DuBois made his first trip to Africa in 1921, after the end of the Pan African Congress. During the trip, he more or less fell in love with Africa. 'The world brightens as it darkens', were his words."

"Well the world sho 'nuff going to explode in brightness soon, cause it is plenty dark right now. Humans suffering from floods, drought, wildfires for days, earthquakes, -Katrina victims still homeless and the earthling folks in a war that never should have been started, - thousands young folk killed, thousand more maimed for life, and jus' think of all the civilians in I-raq killed. If the darkest hour is before dawn, dawn must be right around the corner."

145

"After DuBois' experience in Africa he realized that he had to change his ideological approach to the race problem in America. The Russian Revolution of 1917 drastically affected his thinking. His trip to Russia in 1927, his learning about Marx and Engels and his knowing the importance of the role of class, actually was DuBois' Communist beginnings."

"I like the way he never stopped writing about imperialism, especially in Africa. And he held the fifth Pan African Congress in1945 and what a collection of men folks, but I must say that they definitely should have had some women folk present. Just like when he started the Niagara Movement, twenty-nine men, humpf, why not some women. Sexism raised its ugly head again, even with people progressive and smart as those men folks."

"At that conference was:
>Kwame Nkrumah—Father of Ghanaian independence, first President of Ghana and Pan African Activist
>George Padmore—called the "Father of African Emancipation"
>Jomo Kenyatta—called the "Burning Spear" and first President of Kenya

Now jus' think how more powerful that would have been with:
>Claudia Jones—Trinidadian born radical journalist and full time organizer for the U.S. and British Communist parties and led the international campaign to free Nelson Mandela
>Queen Mother Audley Moore—revolutionary Pan-Africanist, founded the Universal Association of Ethiopian Women
>Raya Dunayevskaya—Russian born Marxist humanist philosopher, political activist, and a pioneering theoretician in the American New Left advocating the recognition of the Third World as a revolutionary force in the contemporary era

Women folk bring new and different perspectives to all talks. White folks feared that Blacks will be equal to them in smartness,

146

economics, and politics, and men folks feared women in the same way. Keep them down so they can never catch up wit you."

Malcolm nodded in agreement simultaneously giving Sojourner his customary look that of acknowledging the wit and wisdom in her words. "Those two architects of freedom for Blacks, and Garvey too, gave voice and took actions against great odds and that's one of the lessons that should be learned."

"Yes, but in learning dose lessons, again, don't leave out the women." And at this point Sojourner shook that walking stick in Malcolm's direction. "Amy Jacques Garvey, Mr. Garvey's 2nd wife, let me tell you about not only her but the role of women in the Universal Negro Improvement Association, (UNIA). In Kingston, Jamaica, before UNIA came to America, about half the members were women. When the headquarters moved to New York, women held some of the highest positions in the movement. The head of UNIA's printing press was a woman named Lillian Galloway. An African-American actress, Henrietta Vinton Davis became an international organizer.

Now Amy Jacques Garvey, she was something else. She was an editor, race activist and what we would call a feminist today. When Marcus Garvey was convicted and incarcerated for mail fraud in connection with his Black Star shipping line, - the guv'ment had to get him for something 'cause as a Black man he was too powerful to be allowed to continue – well, Amy raised funds for his defense, published two volumes of his speeches and writings and acted as his personal representative while he was in prison After his release from prison he was deported from the USA never to return again.

She was the associate editor of The Negro World, and introduced a new page called, Our Women and What They Think, which carried international news about the status of women, poetry, profiles of leading Black women and Black female historical figures, and a column by and about members of the women's auxiliary. She was a leading Pan Africanist and a driving force behind UNIA. Now having done all that, please tell me why when you read and hear 'bout the feminist woman   in history, - you don't read about Amy alongside Rosa Luxemburg, the Grimke sisters, Susan B. Anthony and Elizabeth Cady Stanton. How come? I'll tell you how come, because of history's short sightedness when it comes to giving Black women their just due and because the Black feminist doesn't do all her homework."

"Teach Sister, teach. Shall we call it Women's Studies 101, Black History 102 on the college level or general studies for the curriculum for all high school students? It's quite true. Women in general and Black women in particular have been neglected or given a back seat to men. Speaking of a Black dimension, one of the women that you said should have been involved in the Pan American Congress, Raya Dunayevskaya, keenly understood the Black dimension in women's liberation as well as in world struggles. She was a brilliant thinker and I quote one of her words, *"To grasp the Black dimension is to learn a new language, the language of thought. Black thought. For many, the new language will be difficult because they are hard of hearing. Hard of hearing because they are not used to this type of thought, a language which is both a struggle for freedom and the thought of freedom'.* In addition, all students should be required to read her book, American Civilization on Trial Black Masses as Vanguard. It is a pamphlet style publication of one hundred and seventeen pages of provocative but true, amazingly concise and revealing story of the roles of Blacks as vanguards in American history.

America has all the ingredients it needs for excellence in education. We have the materials for the physical plants, an over load of teaching materials and books, enough food to feed those children in need of breakfast and lunch, enough money to train and pay teachers properly. It just isn't profitable enough for capitalism. Simple as that."

"Well, Professor Malik Shabazz, this discussion is charging our innards. We done laid all the problems out before us. We can't overlook the progress made in the past years since the Little Rock Nine but we must keep it moving. And we must keep a sharp

148

watch on that Supreme Court because they the ones trying to move the little progress wc made backwards. And please, don't continue with that no chile left behind or we will have ALL the chilluns left behind."

Malcolm gave a mock salute and smile to Sojourner. Their morning stroll was bringing them to a section of the retreat that housed a wide variety of radicals, Musicians Mansion and Poets Pavilion.

Chapter Seven Glossary and Endnotes

- *Billie Holiday (1915-1959):* Birth name Eleanora Holiday. One of the greatest musical performers of the century beyond being the offspring of a 13-year old mother and 15-year old father. She changed her name to "Billie" and later in her musical life when she met Lester Young, a great, unique saxophone player, he called her "Lady Day." Billie Holiday led a life of severe hardships, great successes, tragic events, and tremendous stardom. She possessed an inimitable musical style in voice, phrasing and delivery. Her rendition of *"Strange Fruit"* is an epic in itself.

- *Daisy Bates (1914-1999):* Born in Little Rock, Arkansas. Bates was an African American civil rights leader, journalist, publisher and author who played a leading role in the Little Rock integration crisis of 1957. Her mother was murdered while resisting three local white men who were attempting to rape her. Her father left the family shortly after and Daisy was raised by friends. She married at an early age and with her husband published a local Black newspaper, *The Arkansas State Press.* The paper was an avid voice for civil rights.

- *Susan B. Anthony (1820-1906):* A prominent American civil rights leader played a pivotal role in the 19th century Woman' Rights Movement in introducing women's suffrage to the United States. Born in Adams, Massachusetts. She traveled the United States and Europe giving over 100 speeches a year for 45 years championing suffrage, abolition, temperance and equal rights.

- *Elizabeth Cady Stanton (1815-1902):* Stanton was an American social activist and leading figure of the early Women's Movement. She and Susan B. Anthony formed the National Women's Suffrage Association in 1869. They were two of the most famous influential women rights leaders of their times. Unfortunately later in their political careers they moved further away from universal suffrage and their language became increasingly racist and classist.

- *Tom Joyner:* Born November, 1949 - Joyner is an African American radio host with a daily program syndicated across the United States and heard by over 10 million radio listeners. He regularly donates funds to Historically Black Colleges and offers individual scholarships.

- The Song "*Strange Fruit*" was written by Lewis Allen a poet working as a high school teacher. His real name was Abel Meeropol. He later adopted the sons of Julius and Ethel Rosenberg who were executed for treason in 1953. They were exonerated in recent years. Today there is the Rosenberg Fund for Children, for youth whose parents have been targeted for their progressive activities. In April 1939, Allen bought his poem to the club where Billie was performing and played it for her. At first she did not know what to make of it, did not know what the song meant, but once it hit her, as she sang the tears came, they rolled down her cheeks. The impact on the audience was tremendous and Billie identified with it. It became a personal thing and it got to the point where she said, "This is my song." When she sang "Strange Fruit", everything stopped, the waiters were not allowed to serve, and everything was dark except for a small pin spot on her face. She never moved. Her hands were down and she never touched the mike. The tears never interfered with her voice, but the tears would come and knock everybody in the house out. Up to that time, the national magazines did not print pictures of Blacks. Soon after Billie started singing "Strange Fruit", Time magazine came down and printed her picture plus the lyrics and from then on other pictures of Blacks appeared. Source: *Wishing on the Moon, The Life and Times of Billie Holiday,* by Donald Clarke, pgs. 163-165.

- "*History of Rope*". Last three incidents on pg.96 referenced from Leonard Pitts commentary on pg. 9 of St. Croix Avis Newspaper's Sunday-Monday Issue dated Oct. 14-15, 2007.

- Phyllis Wheatley (1753-1784): Poet and Author. References made to her writings by R.R. Lewis-A Coloured Man, 1841— Excerpts taken from the book Light and Truth. *"This distinguished colored young woman was brought a slave from*

151

Africa to America, in the year 1761, when between seven and eight years of age, and sold to Mr. John Wheatley, a respectable citizen of Boston, in whose family she continued to reside. According to his testimony, "without any assistance from school education, with only what she was taught in the family, in sixteen months from the time of her arrival, she attained the English language, to which she was before an utter stranger, to such a degree, as to read any, the most difficult parts of the sacred writings, to the great astonishment of all who heard her."

After she had obtained a very respectable command of the English language, as her writings testify, she was not content with this acquisition. Her master further states, "She has a great inclination to learn the Latin tongue, and has made some progress in it."... In 1772, when she was about seventeen years of age, and had been ten years in America, her poetical · productions, which were written as an amusement in her leisure hours, became known to her friends, who earnestly advised to their publication. Though nothing was further from her thoughts, while composing them, than such a use of them, yet in deference to their judgment and in compliance with their wishes, it was done. The publisher, justly fearful lest the fact should be questioned that these poems were really written by Phyllis, very prudently procured the following attestation: "We, whose names are underwritten, do assure the world, that the poems specified in the following page were (as we verily believe,) written by Phyllis, a young African girl, who was, but a few years since, brought an uncultivated barbarian from Africa, and has ever since been and now is, under the disadvantage of serving as a slave in a family in this town. She has been examined by the best judges, and is thought qualified to write them." This certificate was signed by the existing Governor and Lieutenant Governor of Massachusetts, and by all the most distinguished civilians and clergy of Boston. Among the names is that of John Hancock, the president of the first American Congress.

As the little volume of poems here referred to is, at the present time, rarely to be met with, a few extracts from it may be

152

interesting to our readers, and will be honorable to African genius. Phyllis evinces that her reading has been considerably extensive, for she often alludes to the classic writers of antiquity in a way, which shows that she was not ignorant of their works. The following allusion to the writings of Homer, an Ethiopian, is found in one of her poems:

> While Homer paints, lo! circumfused in air
> Celestial gods in mortal forms appear;
> Swift as they move hear each recess rebound,
> Heav'n quakes, earth trembles, and the shores rebound,
> Great sire of verse, before my mortal eyes,
> The lightnings blaze across the vaulted skies,
> As the thunder shakes the heavenly plains,
> A deep-felt horror thrills through all my veins,
> When gentle strains demand thy graceful song,
> The length'ning line moves languishing along,
> When great Patroclus courts Achilles' aid
> The grateful tribute of my tears is paid:
> Prone on the shores he feels the pangs of love,
> The stern Pelides' tend'rest passions move.

Phyllis's harp was early unstrung on earth, but, it is hoped, to be tuned to sublimer melody in heaven. She died in 1784, aged about 31 years. Her name has obtained an honorable place in the most respectable biographical dictionaries; and those works would probably be searched in vain for an instance of equal improvement under equal disadvantages...

The material about Phyllis Wheatley was taken directly from the book Light and Truth collected from The Bible and Ancient and Modern History of the Colored and the Indian Race: From Creation of the World to the Present Time By R.B. Lewis—A Colored Man

Research this work with care and candor; Every time and page you read will brighten all the truths of scripture, proved by history-plain indeed. Published by a Committee of Colored Gentlemen—Benjamin F. Roberts, Printed 1844

Chapter VIII

Gay Gardens

A large teak, weather-beaten sign – FOR SALE – sat alone on the front lawn of Gay Gardens. One morning, Radclyffe Hall, a self-described 'congenital invert'*, feeling particularly gleeful, exuberant and totally self-accepting, decided to update Gay Gardens by placing the 'FOR SALE' sign at the entrance.

Radclyffe often sat alone in the Gardens reminiscing about her gay past defined by a simplified, generalized, sexual orientation division - heterosexual or homosexual, period. And the word, "gay', included both men and women. When she compared it to today's lexicons – lesbians, gays, bi-sexual, transvestites, transgender, two-spirits, hermaphrodites, queers, - she would ruefully shake her head.

The living dwellings for Gay Gardens was not entirely deserted –it just had a nobody-lives-here-anymore look. Stucco buildings in muted rainbow colors showed off manicured lawns and trimmed hedges with lavender wild flowers and yellow rambling roses keeping tight company with one another as they roamed around the gardens.

This morning Radclyffe sat on a bench with knees drawn up to her chin and her arms clasped around her ankles. She was admiring the iridescent humming birds as they hovered over flowers sipping nectar, when she spotted Malcolm and Sojourner. Radclyffe was dressed in a black trim cut pants suit, a white ruffled front shirt and a wide brimmed black fedora. As the twosome drew near she called out, "Good morning my sister and brother and you can decide which one I am."

Sister Sojourner smiled at Radclyffe saying, "Sister Radclyffe you always are a welcoming sight to these old eyes of mine. A dapper dandy, that's who you are with a flair for being outrageous and that's exactly what the staid population needs at times. When I first laid eyes on that sign I thought that someone with a visionary mind put that sign there and I likened that someone to you."

Radclyffe laughingly responded, "Right again mother Sojourner. And what mischief have you been stirring up this morning brother Malcolm?"

"Sister, it feels so good to be up here free from the troubles of the world that I often hesitate to use the Time Gazer for fear of becoming contaminated by listening to what's going on."

"I must say that when it comes to the gay and lesbian scene some great strides have been taken. However, it is true that in the Retreat we are spared nonsensical behaviors. Gay Gardens has its' fair share of revolutionary -minded people and thankfully we aren't marginalized ."

"Malcolm and Sister Hall, since my arrival in1883, - and I came here like a shooting star- newcomers never did stay very long in Gay Gardens and not because they weren't gay any more but because they weren't different in any biased way. Seems like after a short while the newcomers be they writers, activists, poets, musicians, artists, relocated on the basis of their profession or talents. Most claim to have dual res'dency. Nowadays the gardens is used mostly by any individual wanting a bit of quietness."

Radclyffe invited the duo to join her on the teak veranda that was dignified with large, ceramic pots filled with tiger lilies, spider lilies and hydrangea and furniture made from nature's own bamboo. They were no sooner seated when two part-time residents of the Garden were heard and seen on the pathway.

"As-Salaam Alaikum", greeted Malcolm.

"Walaikum Salaam" proudly returned Mabel Hampton. "Tennessee here, try as he might just can not get the Arabic words to come out without a Southern accent. You know how

156

Southerners can take a three syllable word and have it come out with six or more syllables."

Tennessee Williams with his gentle eyes and darkly handsome visage, smiled and announced, "How y'all doin'? Pay Mabel no attention."

"A healthy greeting is what counts; said Sojourner. "Don't matter what language it's in or how you say it . What counts are the true feelings."

"True, true, Sojourner. Mabel and I were reminiscing about our personal histories and decided to relax in Gay Gardens and, much to our delight, here is Radclyffe plus the two of you."

Radclyffe invited Mabel and Tennessee to join them in conversation. "We were talking about how in the Retreat it's a perfect world with absolutely no room for bigotry, ignorance, and hatred which are the rock bottom basis for discrimination and oppressions of all kinds. On earth we were viewed as outsiders or more frequently outcasts."

"Oh, Radclyffe, it was much worse than that. In the past lesbians who were 'out' ran the risk of being institutionalized in a mental hospital, imprisonment, losing their jobs and being attacked physically. When I was 8 years old I left my home with relatives on account of being sexually abused and poor treatment. I lived with a white family until I was 17, but in my later life managed to live a reasonable 'out' life for a lesbian in the 20's and '30's"

"Mabel Hampton you were quite an exception," said Tennessee, "and one hell of an inspiration for all lesbians to come! I find it particularly intriguing that your main survival mechanism was being yourself."

"Being true to oneself is a virtue in itself. How'd you manage Sis Mabel?"

Tennessee interjected eagerly, "Mabel led a very integrated life, - a very well defined lesbian life having fallen in love with Lillian Foster and living as a couple for 45 years. She maintained a household that participated in activities that were proper and necessary at the times. Mabel, Lillian and friends, gay and straight, were active in World War II. Mabel was her community's air raid warden, and she was active in the Civil rights Movement and the Stonewall Rebellion. According to her liking and interests she attended performances by the Negro National Opera Company. In the Roaring 20's she found work dancing in an all women's troupe in Coney Island, New York."

Mabel was in her usual comfortable attire- wide legged grey cargo pants, a classic Vanilla French cuff blouse, with a jazzy brown and tan checkered vest and brown faux suede mid-calf boots and of course, the cap, - a corduroy, brown apple cap with the peak pulled down over her left eye. She pushed the cap back a bit then pulled it further to the left side. "My good friends", she began, "I've been a lesbian for 82 years and was part of a social network that was not exclusively lesbian. I was/am basically a woman who fell in love with a woman and since men and marriage were not part of what I wanted in life, I excluded them."

"In one sense Mabel, you were ahead of your time. You had a gay common law marriage."

"No, no, now wait a minute Radclyffe." Mabel drummed her fingers on her thigh as she spoke "During my days on earth, I lived my life as I felt I should and formal, orthodox marriage was not on my agenda. Today there's a great deal of opposition to gay marriages and for the likes of me I don't know why gays and lesbians would want to be part of an institution that has a 50% failure rate. I beamed down on an article by a Charley Reese and he said, and I echo 'if you are against gay marriage then don't marry a gay person'. Simple as that. My feelings on the subject are, gay or straight, if you want to get married, be my guest. If you don't, you can also be my guest."

"All your behaviors, Ms. Hampton", chortled Sojourner, "sounds radical and revolutionary to me, especially during that time. And you had the good sense or the good habit, of keeping your letters, articles, clippings from papers and magazines, - you were a collector and little did you know at the time how important it was because later you gave them to the Lesbian Herstory Archives. That was a mighty important contribution."

Radclyffe leaned over and plucked a rambling rose, examined it for suitability, - satisfied, she placed it in the band of her fedora. "Just keeping up with my 'dandy dude' appearance, Sojourner. What has truly interested me of late is the number of psychological and sociological research, studies and experiments conducted as well the introduction of new therapies, with almost all of them ending up with incomplete or contradictory results.

"Is there a gay gene or several genes that interact with non genetic factors that causes homosexuality? Is it by choice? Then on the basis of these assumptions treatments follow, and all for what? Well for one thing so the pharmaceutical companies and therapists can make money with their claims that they can *cure* us as if we had some disease."

"Speaking of *cures* on a personal note imagine going through life being your natural, normal self and being considered by others to be unnatural and abnormal. Its right up on the top rungs of the nonsense ladder with assumptions like being inferior if you're non-white, or beauty being based on European features and silky, blonde hair. In no way did I need to be cured. It's all harmful, prejudice foolishness. What a blessing to be here among sane people in a sane environment," added Mabel.
"Yes indeed, 'tis a blessing, but the real true blessing will be when there is no more need for all the marching, the parades, the protests and street battles with police and court battles for justice and equality," responded Sojourner.

"Yes, however like all struggles to overcome oppressive conditions, it takes courageous pioneers, leaders, plus constituents,

- masses of folks, whether initially they fully understand the theory or don't , get bodies behind you and teach as you move your agenda forward."

Tennessee chimed in before Malcolm had hardly finished his sentence. "Corporate America constantly operates to derail such actions and one very important part of that machinery is the 'homo-patriarch'. It's a term coined by an author connoting the connection between homosexual behaviors and patriarchy, with specific reference to males in America's ruling class, their bonding and same- sex proclivity and activities."

"Listen closely and with a fine tuned ear, 'cause here comes Tennessee with some of his emotional and erotic reality talks," quipped Hall.

"This white, male bastion of power demonstrates homosexual cohesiveness and behaviors, -hence the term, homo-patriarch. The same-sex bonding, socializing, net working, friendships and relationships that exist between and among the patriarch is so 'gay' that there is a concentrated movement to divert public attention from their same-sex behavior and disguise it with safe, acceptable, elitist terms. They systematically heighten the taboo around the gay community and express contempt and aversion. Thou protest too much, oh homo-patriarch."

Mabel cocked her head toward Tennessee as she queried, "What's that you're saying that male leadership and the ole boys club are the seat and heart of gay society?"
"Not exactly. What I'm saying is, - well, look at the following male groups and events; fraternities, stag parties, athletic teams, the Masons, the Elks, the priesthood, and above all the Bohemian Grove with their yearly ritual and you will observe same sex intimacy behaviors among them."

"From my inner city days I am familiar with male boisterous behavior. I know about stag parties and among athletes I see all that butt slapping, hugging, chest bumping, and those wrestlers can

160

apply some holds that Kama Sutra could use in their books on erotic positions and it sure involves same sex pleasures, but tell me more about this Bohemian Grove."

Tennessee lightly fingered his faded brown corduroy trousers and with a twinkle in his eyes began, "My information may not be the latest and I'm not sure of what exactly goes on today, because it's difficult to beam in on their activities. At one time this elite organization, the Bohemian Grove, wanted to ban airplanes from flying over the grove property' Like a no fly zone. It makes me think of Chief Seattle's speech, 'How Can One Sell the Air?'"

Malcolm and Sojourner seated on their paisley cushioned bamboo seats wore curious expressions as Tennessee continued.

"The Bohemian Grove is the property of the Bohemian Club of San Francisco. The Grove is located 65 miles north of San Francisco amidst twenty seven hundred acres of giant California redwoods. The Club's most famous event represents the epitome of the homosexual social cohesiveness of America's ruling class. Approximately 1500 men gather annually for a two week retreat, an encampment for the rich and famous and those holding to political positions including ex-presidents. There is entertainment, food, and drink of the supreme order with furnishings and recreation to ones individual tastes.

A rather strange ceremony that has taken place since 1880, consisted of an elaborate play with a moral message that centers on inevitable human frailty. It opens with a procession of men dressed in pointed red hoods and red flowing gowns, accompanied by men playing dirge funeral music and others carrying lighted torches. It's high drama, an elaborate spectacle, far too detailed to offer further description. The main point is that these men engage in shenanigans with a degree of intimacy, cohesiveness that is not unlike a beaux-arts ball. It is all done on a very, very sophisticated level and at prodigious costs."

"Sounds like debauchery to me. Excuse my language Sojourner, but is this the place I read about where the men have pissing contests? Anyway, let me know when their next high jinks are taking place so I can try to beam them up."

"You calling them high jinks, Mabel when you don't even know the reasons for their actions."

"Sojourner, I agree with Mabel", supported Malcolm, "It sure does sound like outrageous antics and I'll bet many of the participants are in the closet."

"Friends, don't rush to judgment. Who knows what spirit moves those men. Mabel and Radclyffe, you were pioneers and tested the waters publicly. The Bohemian Grove men may not be so courageous, that's why they hide things. During my preaching days, I was often ridiculed and taunted with the accusation that I was a man, as if being of any sex is grounds for ridicule. But my message to the world was as much a part of me, as any one of my limbs and I continued to preach and live the words of my religion. You women were true to yourselves. Those Bohemian Grove men are true to some belief or they wouldn't be acting the way they do."

"All true Sojourner, but the Bohemian Grove, at least to my way of thinking, has to be seen in terms of its power to influence America's social and political systems and to that extent their beliefs must be questioned. Are they using their power for the benefit of all or largely for themselves?"

"Tennessee is really on to something. We all need to beam in on that group, even if some of those giant redwoods have to be trimmed down so we can see all the socially kinky behavior", laughed Radclyffe.

"Radclyffe you were born in Great Briton in 1880 and that's the year recognized as the beginning of the ritual with the red cloaked men. Just a coincidence. Your life story is outstanding in terms of

162

your being 'out'. Most people know you for your novel <u>The Well of Loneliness</u>, the only one of your eight novels that had an overt lesbian theme. You were a novelist, poet, and short story writer but it was your personal love life that set the world ablaze."

"Mabel, it was blazing and intriguing", intoned Tennessee. "Radclyffe, you could readily be called a womanizer. What I truly admirer in both you and Mabel, in addition to your courage was your attire. You wore what you damn pleased and felt comfortable and satisfied."

"Mabel and I had a lot in common when it comes to troubled childhood and being an 'out' lesbian. Mabel's hardships were largely due to poverty and race and my being born into wealth did not protect me from the emotional neglect of a philandering father, divorced parents and being ignored by a mother and step-father.

But when it comes to women in our lives, I am so far ahead of Mabel it's like a snail in a race with a jackrabbit. At age 27, I met a 51-year-old married woman, - a mother, and grandmother, a lieder singer, and we fell in love, eventually set up a residence, and lived together for years. Then I fell in love with her cousin who was an admiral's wife and mother of a young daughter. That relationship lasted until my death but in between, I had other love affairs. In retrospect, I lived the life that was allowed me and I'm grateful for it."

"Radclyffe, how you got away with it all I do not know, but my hat's off to both you and Mabel for playing so well the cards life dealt you."

"Tennessee Williams, spoken like a trouper. You were born in Columbus, Mississippi, 1911, weren't you, and entered the Retreat in 1985. How come they didn't call you Mississippi Williams", chided Malcolm.

"I was born Thomas Lanier Williams. I moved to New Orleans in 1939 and changed my name to 'Tennessee' the state of my father's birth. It didn't matter what they called me, I still was the gay southerner, - a victim of rampant homophobia."

"And that was a shame", said Hampton. "Everybody, well almost everybody, is familiar with the <u>Glass Menagerie</u> and <u>Street Car Named Desire,</u> both written by my celebrated playwright and Pulitzer Prize winning friend. Yet my man Tennessee had to withstand a vicious onslaught from some members of the literary establishment. As I think of all the pain and suffering inflicted upon gays and lesbians, I think the earthling's gays and lesbians should start their drive for reparations."

"Reparations! How you going to pay people back for being mistreated Mabel? How?", interjected Radclyffe.

Sojourner responded, "listen to me chillums—after the Civil War, I worked wit the free slaves and had the opportunity to understand more fully how the lives of my people were used for the enrichment of others. The vast and manifold contributions that Black people had made to the development of the United States had yet to be acknowledged or rewarded. I said then and I'll say now, 'Our nerves and sinews, our tears and blood, have been sacrifices on the altar of this nation's avarice. Our unpaid labor has been a stepping stone to financial success. Some of its dividends must surely be ours'."

"Thank you Sister Sojourner", extolled Mabel. "In some form or the other there should be pay back for such deliberate mistreatment. Just think of Matthew Shepard and what he and his family went through."

"Oh, who among us can forget that? Ten years ago, 21 year old Matthew, a gay college student at the University of Wyoming, was brutally beaten his skull fractured in six places and his body lashed to a fence in a lonely spot out of town."

"Tennessee, now you know there should be some retribution for the victim even though the two men who committed that dastardly hate crime murder are serving life sentences."

"Radclyffe, you pay them back by giving compensation in one form or the other for mistreatment. Look a here, now, the Jews of the Holocaust received some reparations; the Japanese for their treatment during World War II, when they were locked up in animal stalls and all that. The Native Americans were given casino grounds and rights that in my opinion were tickets to more drunkenness and poverty, and the African-Americans are talking about reparations because of slavery. If you consider the treatment of gays---when I say gays I mean lesbians too--- received, it's comparable to the mistreatment the other groups suffered. Gays were murdered, beaten, burned at the stakes, denied jobs, evicted from houses, ostracized, denigrated and stigmatized. And who allowed it? The government and institutional and individual homophobia. So the entire society owes us reparations."

"If all who were mistreated had to receive this compensation, does that serve as salvation for those who mistreated them? Like you pay for forgiveness?"

Mabel answered, "It's not about forgiveness Radclyffe, it's about recognition of wrong deeds and compensation for such. The compensation need not be monetary. It could be the establishment and enforcement of certain laws, or scholastic scholarships or free educational opportunities or housing."

"I was talking with Harvey Milk the other day and he was saying that the public needs to be better informed about the heart searing unimaginable soul shattering experiences of gays and lesbians and the proliferation of hate crimes against gays. One only needs to read Leslie Steinberg's <u>Stone Butch Blues</u> to have an understanding of the travails of trying to live a life that is in opposition to your natural self," added Tennessee.

"On an up note", said Radclyffe, "today's gays and lesbians have access to activities, events and opportunities that were unthinkable in my time. There's the Gay games, T.V. shows starring lesbians like the Ellen Degeneres show and *Olivia*. Olivia Travel: Cruises, Resorts, and Vacations for Lesbians. Olivia is the premier lesbian travel company providing amazing vacations for women. With their *feel free* slogan women can travel to places all over the world, - Alaska, the Greek Isles, Tahiti, the Caribbean, Australia, - and on four and five star cruise lines with superb accommodations, activities, and entertainment. Think of the miles and miles of difference between reading The Well of Loneliness, hidden in a plain brown wrapper and Olivia Travel being broadly publicly advertised on television, websites, worldwide."

"On the entertainment circuit for years now I have been watching the lesbian theatrical team of Peggy Shaw and Lois Weaver. Their company is called Split Britches."

"What kind of name is that Tennessee?"

"Sojourner, the name is taken from a garment worn by Lois Weaver's ancestors in the Blue Ridge Mountains of Virginia. It's an undergarment that is split so the women could pee."

"Is that right?" Sojourner said cocking her head. "Women's garments are so often hindersome. I can see why some women took to wearing clothes designed for men."

Tennessee continued, "Peggy and Lois are independent performance artists. Peggy Shaw is a painter and poet as well and a supremely superb solo performer. Their company's performances challenges established practices in theaters as they challenge the political status quo. I was particularly intrigued when they did a show titled *Tennessee Waltz* that was sort of based on one of my plays."

"Now I like what I'm hearing", said Malcolm. "Innovative and creative women, challenging the status quo. Tennessee, keep me informed so I can beam in on Split Britches. That's some name."

"Homophobia, reparations, Stonewall Rebellion and Olivia Cruises, Split Britches, Ellen Degeneres, - all part of the American history that requires documentation, and needs to continue their progressive movements. The Earth folks have a heap of work to do. They need to re-examine their need to violate and disrespect others," Sojourner spoke resolutely.

The quintet – Mabel, Tennessee, Radclyffe, Malcolm and Sojourner, -watched as one, as two mourning doves circled around the veranda then scurried across the lawn and settled down directly in front of the group. Soft grey was the dominant color of their full breasts, as they fluttered about, slight brown speckles showed on their wings. They eyed one another and began their plaintive cooing back and forth, similar to a call and response. They seemed impervious to the humans, yet they seemed to be engaged in a performance for them. The doves skittered with their inimitable short-legged bird movements, emitting their mourning sounds at regular intervals. The group sat entranced until several moments later the doves took flight, circling above the five, leaving the echoes of their mourning cries in the air.

"Is that a sign or not," exclaimed Mabel. "I'd like it to be the mourning of the death of homophobia."

"Well we know doves represent peace or peaceful policies, politically speaking, so they may be the harbinger of a change in attitudes toward gays and lesbians and transgenders, all," Tennessee added quietly.

Speaking in subdued tones Radclyffe said, "I think it's a reminder to us to be gentle and to be in harmony with others, same sex or different sex. They were a male and female couple, weren't they? Or maybe they were same sex doves."

Sojourner concluded, "Religiously speaking, doves are a representation of the Holy Spirit. I find that to be a fitting ending to a subject that needs much attending to. So let us rejoice in being blessed by two of God's lovely creatures."

Upon that note, Sojourner rose, Malcolm followed saying to the others, "Stay settled, and digest the happening."

The twosome reluctantly moved down the pathway making their way towards Inventor's Enclave.

Chapter Eight Glossary and Endnotes

- *Congenital invert*: A term taken from the writings of Havelock Ellis and other sexologists.; Denotes homosexuality.
- *Harvey Milk (1930-1978):* A San Francisco city politician who helped open the door for gays and lesbian in the United States by championing civil rights for homosexuals. He was murdered in 1978, the victim of a hate crime. Milk is regarded as a symbol of activism. He was not a one- issue politician and battled for a wide range of social changes in education, public transportation, child care and low-income housing.
- *George Moscone (1929-1978):* George Moscone was an American attorney, Democratic politician and elected Mayor of San Francisco, California in 1976. He and Harvey Milk were assassinated/murdered, November 27, 1978 by a disgruntled politician, Dan White.
- *Matthew Shepard (1977-1998):* Matthew Shepard was a gay college student at the University of Wyoming in Laramie, Wyoming. He was severely beaten and his 5 foot 2, 105 pound body was found lashed to a fence outside of town. His murder was an act of violence against homosexuals and the two men who murdered him are serving life sentences in prison.
- *Charles Reese*: A columnist whose articles appear in various daily newspapers. The referenced comment was published in *The St. Croix Avis Newspaper* on Tuesday, June 24, 2008 pg. 9.

Chapter IX

Inventors' Enclave

Three figures formed a silhouette against a bank of low, puffy, cotton ball like clouds, - cumulus clouds. The person in the middle of the trio was styling and profiling to the amusement of the others. His attire was ridiculously audacious. Knickers in a daring combination of melon and green plaid polyester-cotton met below the knees by a pair of fuchsia socks. An Italian cashmere argyle vest in cardinal red, canary yellow and white was a perfect mismatch for the pants. A short sleeve tan polka dot polo shirt embroidered with black golf balls showed off his sculpted sun darkened arms. Black and white saddle shoes and a tartan plaid cap completed the outfit.

"Brother Grant, what in the name of all that is heavenly in our domain is that outfit all about? You look like I don't know what." T.J Marshall snickered as he addressed Grant.

"I am going to declare my rightful position in the golf world. My contribution has been too long neglected."

"With that blazing outfit I'll have to use my invention to protect you from incinerating yourself," said T. J. Marshall who invented the fire extinguisher in 1872. And if that doesn't work", he continued, "I'll call J.W. Smith, inventor of the lawn sprinkler to help me."

The third member of the trio, Madame C.J. Walker shook her head in mild disbelief as she gave Grant a look over. "George Grant, with that outfit I don't know what world would want to claim you."

It was early morning, beautiful clouds overhead and the sounds of mourning doves cooing surrounded the trio as they conversed near their duplex in Inventor's Enclave. The building was both ostentatious and mellow. This may seem improbable but one side of the dwelling's construction had partitions with all sorts of angles jutting in all directions and in metallic colors. The other side as if in contempt or contrast consisted of smooth layered pine in soft pastels. Zora Neale Hurston called it a 'colossal catastrophe'.

"Madame Walker", began Grant, "you are a celebrity. You are well known throughout the country as America's first woman millionaire, - that is, one who didn't inherit a fortune or marry into it, -you are also the first Black woman millionaire -the woman who developed the "hot comb" to straighten kinky hair as well as developing a cosmetic business and a string of beauty schools. You have your due recognition."

"You are right brother Grant, I was an inventor, manufacturer, marketer and millionaire, but I want to make it clear that my invention of the hot comb, and incidentally, the idea came from my job as a laundress, the heat of an iron ironing out wrinkles so why not heat to straighten kinky or super curly hair – was not to encourage Black women to have straight hair like white women, but to introduce Black women to the world of cosmetology and beauty schools based on their specific genetic composition. And as you know, the Mme. C.J. Walker Manufacturing Co. Inc. still exists."

"Now you know Madame Walker many Black women wanted that 'straight hair', that 'blow hair', the kind that blows in the wind", interjected T.J. Marshall.

"Alright, T.J., some women definitely wanted straighter hair and couldn't care less about genetic compositions, but nonetheless, I introduced Walker's beauty schools along with the hot comb."

"That's what I'm talking about. You developed the "Walker System of Beauty" that taught Black women health and beauty tips and – like Avon, trained them to sell products door to door. Now on the other hand, how many people know of George Grant the inventor?"

"How many people know that there's hardly a thing in their homes that was not invented by a Black person? Not many. Blacks themselves don't know the extent of their creativity." T.J. Marshall dressed in beige slacks and matching sport shirt continued looking at Grant in amused admiration.

George Grant tapped his lips three times with his index finger, nodded gently at his friends and declared, "Folks I am about to remedy that situation when it comes to golf." With self-importance he asked, "How many golfers are there in America?"
Sarah Walker and T.J. simultaneously said. "I don't know."

"I don't know either. But, we all know that there's a whole heap of them out there. Thousands playing every day at magnificent golf courses and at scruffy divot ridden nine-hole pastures, and each time they tee off, - with the only exception I know of, big Laura Davies from England, - all the golfers tee off with **my** invention. And do they say, 'thank you Georgie; or God bless Mr. Grant'? No, because they don't know of me.

As a golfer, I became frustrated trying to keep the ball stationary prior to a swing. So on December 2, 1899, I patented a golf tee that raised the ball slightly off the ground enabling the player greater control with his wooden club. My tee was made of a small wooden peg with a concave piece of rubber on top to hold the ball. And today my invention has become a standard piece of equipment for all golfers."

"So what do you intend to do and why is Laura Davies an exception and I still want an explanation for your outfit."

"T.J., Laura Davies is an exception because she just hacks a hunk of earth with a club, sets her ball down, and slam bam the ball goes for miles. Now here is my plan. Edmonia Lewis and Augusta Savage are two of the many famous sculptors up here. Edmonia is busy sculpting four new faces a la Mt. Rushmore of Eugene Debs, Mother Jones, Frederick Douglass, and Harriet Tubman, for the

172

Native American community. I have contacted Augusta Savage to sculpt a three foot high statue of me in bronze."

"In bronze? Then why are you wearing all those colors? Grant, have you gone daft?"

Between spurts of laughter Grant admitted, "I know you two are puzzled but the outfit is a gimmick. The same way you two are gazing at me in wonderment, golf players will do the same. Once the sculpture is completed Romare Bearden will do the colors."

Madame Walker in a stylish dusty rose knit top with a delicately ornamented V neck and a dusty rose crinkled skirt shifted her weight and cocked her marcel-waved head to the side and responded, "Romare was an excellent choice since he was a collage-artist as well as a celebrated and influential artist, painter, well known for the jazz musicians that he painted as part of his documentation of black American life. But George, why put paint over bronze?"

"Alright, alright, I'll leave it up to Augusta and Romare to determine the best medium", conceded Grant.

"We still don't know what you are going to do with the statue", said Marshall.

"Listen carefully, here's the grand plan that will give me my long overdue recognition. I am going to prepare, in advance a statue to be placed in golf shops worldwide. At the base of it will be an inscription detailing my great contribution to the golfing world. Now, just look at this pose for the statue."

Grant picked up a golf club nearby, leaned on it, crossed his legs at the ankles, and in his other hand held out an over sized white tee. "Attractive, - right?"

"Definitely noticeable, but George you know we don't have direct contact with the earthly world so why all this worldly production of your statue?"

Speaking rapidly and with assurance Grant expounded, "As the Boy Scout slogan goes, 'be prepared', and like the battery commercial, 'ever ready', that's what ole Georgie here is doing. When we can make direct contact with the earth and its inhabitants, immediately I will be prepared and ready— and able to peddle my product."

"That product being a vivid colorama statue of you holding an over sized tee."

"Correct, Madame Walker, and here's how I'm going to market MY product. Eventually it will be a franchise."

I will start exhibiting my statue in a golf shop on the Island of St. Croix, U.S. Virgin Islands. I consider St. Croix to be one of the most beautiful islands, with its unspoiled beauty, - white sand beaches, spectacular reefs, trade winds keeping it climate comfy, and all of this in a lush, unique tropical setting. This will be the first golf course featuring the statue."

"That island is approximately nine miles by twenty-one with a population of about 60 thousand so how will you gain worldwide recognition?"

"I've done my homework. There are a goodly number of tourists and snowbirds who regularly vacation on the Island and play golf at the Buccaneer Golf Course. When they return to their homes all over the states and beyond, they will be talking about the statue of Grant and his major contribution to golf. Via the Earth Gazer, I searched for the club that would be receptive of my statue, plus, I think I have some relatives from the Grant family tree down there.

The Buccaneer is a real popular golf course on St. Croix because of its friendly ambiance and good mixture of players. There's two groups I enjoy watching regularly, -a young, white, female -Pam Kantowski; a Black, female, Crucian, senior citizen; and a middle-age, white, male-Jeff Lee, touted to be one of the best all strikers on the island. Pam, Gloria, and Jeff, that's their names. And a Friday mornings group, Rafa Bonet, a Puerto Rican with a great sense of humor, Diane Burns one of the best female ball strikers on the island and Gloria again. You'd think with all the good players Gloria plays with she would have a lower handicap, but she's working on it. I also like the group of old timers, - the fossils- they take forever to play a round but I thoroughly enjoy watching them."

Madame Walker questioned, "Sure sounds like a great cultural and interracial mixture, but who this most open-minded person who runs the pro-shop is? Sure must be tolerant."

Before George could answer, Jan Matzeliger accompanied by Augusta Savage came into view and greeted the trio. Augusta took a step backwards saying, "George Grant, I don't sculpt in colors."

"You don't have to", answered Grant. "We have already solved that question. Augusta, I'll have a club in one hand and in the other, I'll be holding an assortment of tees, free for the taking. The golf club where your magnificent sculpture will showcase is the Buccaneer and the manager is Tim Johnston, who runs a near perfect golf shop along with Jeannie, his wife. Tim has a devilish sense of humor and can be a bit cantankerous at times, but dealing daily with golfers sure ain't no picnic."
"George I thought the sculpture was for the entrance to Inventors Enclave. What's this nonsense about it being in a pro shop?"

"Augusta let me briefly explain," said C.J. Marshall. "My friend George Grant, with all his heavenly time, is preparing for the moment when we can directly contact earth. He is preparing to showcase himself and his invention in golf shops throughout the world."

"He's doing all this over a sliver of wood, a teeny, slice of lumber! Give me a break", exhorted Jan. "George make sure you include The Clearview Golf Club that is the only known golf course in America that is built, owned and managed by a Black, William J. Powell. His daughter, Rene Powell, is the head professional at the family's club. She is one of only three African American women ever to play in the LPGA (Ladies Professional Golf Association)."

"I'll be sure to put that one on my list. I just hope it's not in a cow pasture."

Unfazed, George simply twirled his golf club like a baton to the amusement of all.

C.J. Walker invited Jan and Augusta to join the group and pulled up chairs forming a semi-circle. Jan Matzeliger said that he and Augusta were returning from a morning walk and wouldn't mind stopping a while before going to Ida's Place.

Augusta Savage was a Harlem Renaissance sculpture and art educator. She encountered many obstacles to her art because of her race, sex, and poverty. Although she had an outstanding reputation as a sculptor of famous and humble people, she supported herself as an educator. This morning she appeared pensive yet appealing in a pink lace tunic and bejeweled jeans.

Augusta Savage continued the conversation saying, "The golf tee is important Grant, but it is also very important that younger generations know of the contributions of Black inventors in general. It would without a doubt raise the self-esteem of the Black youngsters and help diminish negative stereotypes about Blacks."

Jan held a great deal of compassion for Augusta knowing that in despair over her works not selling she destroyed some of them. She had created a major statue, "The Harp", inspired by James Weldon and Rosamond Johnson's "Lift Every Voice and Sing", also known as the Negro National Anthem, for the 1939 World's Fair in

Queens, New York. She could not afford to cast the piece in Bronze so after the fair closed it was destroyed.

Grant profiling again, stood up gesturing with much arm flourishing, "That's the point I'm making. The earthlings need to be educated about inventors. Start with the classroom and I know Augusta will agree with me. They still use pencil sharpeners and ink pens don't they? Well on every pencil sharpener let there be a picture and name of the inventor: John Lee Love; on the typewriter, pictures of Burridge and Marshman; on fountain pens, W.B. Purvis; on every gas mask, hair straightener crème and traffic light, Garrett Morgan."

"We get the picture, George. So shall we move on to the household, - egg beater, lemon squeezer, window cleaner, caps for bottles and jars, curtain rod support, label them all with the names of the inventors?", Marshall enumerated facetiously.

Amidst the humorous responses, an unmistakable New England accented voice interrupted the ongoing conversation, "Good morning to all. Sounds like an inventor's convention. If so you can't exclude old Eli Whitney or my leading lady Hedy Lamarr."

Hedy and Eli had been sitting on the other side of the "colossal catastrophe" on sling back leather chairs permanently placed on either side of a life size replica of Eli Whitney's cotton gin. They readily joined the semi-circle of jovial members of Revolutionary's Retreat.

Jan Matzeliger was born in Paramaribo, then Dutch Guyana, now known as Surinam. His father was a Dutch engineer and his mother a native Black Surinamese. Matzeliger with a wicked smirk on his handsome visage commented, "Whitney your problem as an inventor is to get the public straight on the question of your race. You know how many people and many of them learned, still think of you as a Black inventor? Even in some Black American history books, you are labeled as a Black man who invented the cotton gin. Many Black Americans and Blacks in other countries and members of other ethnic groups believe that you, Eli, were a Black man. This misinformation has been passed on from generation to generation and maybe you should have a session with George Grant to educate the public. "

"I know, I know. I was born in Massachusetts and both parents, - mother, white, father, white, - but somehow their son, Eli is widely known as Black. I imagine part of the reason is the fact that the cotton gin was a mechanical device that removed the seeds from the cotton. Prior to my invention the seeds had to be removed by hand, extremely time consuming, labor intensive and oh so hard on the hands. Since almost exclusively Blacks did this labor, it was reasonable to think that a Black person invented it. At the time, my major woes were associated with imitations of my machine and I was unable to make any profit. There were so many legal battles I had to fight. I filed for my patent in 1794, and it wasn't upheld in court until 1807. There were so many immoral, conniving imitators."

"When it comes to patents many of the Black inventors did not get credit for their inventions for the same reasons. At times their owners stole their inventions, or registered the patents under their own names and other times the government simply did not register their products for any bogus reason."

"Well we can't all use a costume to make our inventions known nationwide."

"T.J. what costume?" asked Hedy, then upon spotting Grant's outfit she did a double take exclaiming, "George, I've heard of color clashes but you're giving a new meaning to it."

Augusta joined in, "You know Hedy, these inventors really have nothing new to invent up here. Satisfaction and contentment reigns. When they have serious discussions they come out with things like, 'Oh we don't need to build a better mouse trap we just need to breed less intelligent rodents.' Or else they spend time re-arranging the multitude of inventions in and around the quarters."

178

"Hedy and Eli, Grant has a plan to make earthlings more aware of his invention", explained Jan. "But we all well know, that inventions that were extremely valuable in the past and were major forces in the development of industry are today obsolete, antiquated and forgotten. I was discussing with Augusta this morning that the shoe lathe I invented, the automatic shoe-making machine that revolutionized the making of shoes, well today has a new twist. If shoes don't fit the feet, alter the feet. Tell them what you were saying about styles, Augusta."

Ms. Savage with her strong yet delicate fingers smoothed her jeans and rubbed her forehead before speaking. Her soft, stern tones mesmerized the audience. "In 1883, when Matzeliger invented the lathe the public profited in many ways, mass production of a sorts, thousands of white immigrants left poverty in Europe to work in the prosperous industry in Lynne, Massachusetts, making it the largest manufacturing center in the world. The invention made for less expensive shoes and more styles. Now a days we have so many styles and categories of shoes, - clogs, wedges, sandals, Birkenstocks, sneakers, earth shoes, walkers, - and they come in all sizes, colors and designs. I can understand women's appreciation for shoes, but I will never understand women mutilating, re-designing their *feet,* just so they can wear a certain style shoe."

"They do what?" Eli. "Re-design their feet!" T.J. Marshall. "Not true!" George Grant.

"Last year one of the latest designs in shoes featured a very, very, very, narrow pointed toe. A misogynist had to design them. Anyway, women were having their feet, their toes re-structured so they could wear the latest fashions. Cut, stitch, and re-shape the foot. That in my opinion is nothing short of bodily mutilation."

Hedy and Madame Walker made eye contact, registering disbelief, and a mutual understanding of the type of women's oppression that tries to achieve ersatz beauty standards. A former white beauty queen very familiar with the behind the scenes manipulations to produce 'stars,' Hedy broke the silence that followed Augusta's words saying, "During my 1940's film goddess days, I can't remember any strivings to achieve beauty that was so outrageously self-destructive."

There was a lull in the conversation as each member dallied with thoughts of inventions and consequences.

Finally, Grant said, "Hedy when you arrived here in 2000 and came to our quarters I have to admit that I wondered, 'What's that White Hollywood star doing here?'"

Eli eager to speak for his leading lady, as he affectionately called Hedy, launched into his oft-repeated story of her contributions to the world. More than a famous actress, she was a brilliant inventor. "Hedy was born Hedwig Eva Maria Kiesler in Vienna in 1913."

The silver screen super star had lived to the ripe age of 87. Remnants of her beauty were still traceable. She smiled at Eli, as she brushed strands of her now white once lush auburn hair from her fine boned face. Entertainers and moviegoers remember her, in addition to her six husbands, for her famous statement, 'Any girl can be glamorous. All you have to do is stand still and look stupid!'"

Whitney continued, "Most people know Hedy Lamarr, the movie star, but she invented a secret communication system patented in 1941 that manipulated radio frequencies between transmission and reception so that top- secret messages could not be intercepted. It was a unique anti-jamming device for use against Nazi radar. The system was especially useful for submarines. The technology called spread spectrum, that we use today now takes on many forms and the entire spread spectrum we use today flows from the invention created by 'my leading lady', Hedy Lamarr", Eli finished with a flourishing bow towards the actress.

"Now Eli, you must include the fact that I had the help of composer George Anthell. And while the U.S. government rejected my design, years after my patent had expired Sylvania adapted the design for a device that today speeds satellite communications around the world"

"Furthermore", concluded Eli, "Hedy Lamarr did not receive money, recognition, or credit."

"When women are recognized or receive patents for their inventions it's usually in the field of household appliances and that is quite natural given the fact that with all the drudgery associated with housework the workers would be the ones to invent something to ease the burdensome chores. However, Hedy and many others like Alice Parker, who invented a new and improved gas heating - furnace, and Mary Walton who developed a method of deflecting smoke stack emissions way back in 1879 and also invented a noise reduction system for elevated railroads in New York City, well their inventions clearly show the breadth of women's creative abilities."

"You are so right, Madame Walker", responded Augusta. "Sarah Goode was born in slavery in 1850 and freed after the Civil war. She moved to Chicago and opened a furniture store. Many of her customers lived in small quarters and did not have space for a full-size bed. And what did Miss Sarah do? She designed a bed that would fold up into a cabinet when not in use. So here we have the first African American female inventor to receive a U.S. patent and the invention was born out of household needs and involved architectural technology. Quite a woman was Sarah Goode."

Marshall cleared his throat and adjusted his horn-rimmed glasses as he engaged the group in historical facts about inventions and dates. "Since ethnic identity is not part of a patent application it is practically impossible to know the first Black woman inventor. Ellen F. Eglin of Washington D.C might be the first since she invented a clothes wringer before April 1880. However no patent was issued in her name and she sold the idea to an agent for eighteen dollars."

"You see", interrupted the businesswoman supreme, "that's the result of ignorance and chicanery, and cheating folks out of what is rightfully theirs. The poor woman probably thought it was impossible for her to get a patent and to successfully peddle her product."

"Madame C.J. that was in the 1800's and all women didn't have your business acumen", offered Jan. Matzeliger, his seriousness evident on his distinct Dutch-looking features. "Nonetheless it is true that women inventors like women in all fields, yesterday as well as today have a much more difficult time than men achieving their due recognition"

"Yes, that's why we late revolutionaries have to make sure the earthlings know who made what, when, and their sex and race.

"Grant, the golf tee is important but there is much newer technology in the making of clubs that improves the distance the ball flies so you can't claim all the glory", admonished Eli Whitney. "But I think we all agree that too few know too little about our contributions to society. We have lists of inventors on the walls of the inside entrance to our building and   this information should be known to all, especially students."

"I wholeheartedly agree", said Jan as he and Augusta got up to continue their walk to Ida's Place. T.J Marshall, Madame Walker, Eli, and Hedy decided to go inside to check out the listings. George Grant spotted Malcolm and Sojourner in the distance and decided to wait for them so he could show off his golfing regalia.

Malcolm called out, "As-salaam Alaikum. Am I seeing an apparition in Technicolor?"

George greeted the pair and explained his outfit and intentions.

St. Croix is such a beautiful island but the conditions of some of the schools, - mildew and molds in the classrooms, no air-conditioning where needed, shortage of books, shortage of

182

teachers- shameful, shameful, particularly because it need not be that way. I beamed in and saw that the St. Croix Landmarks Society is having their third annual House tours February 20, 2008. They'll be showing lovely homes on a tour of the Historic North Street Tyler Christiansted Residence. Well when they finish they need to take that same caravan of people to some of those schools with the historic mildew and mold", was Sojourner's comment.

"I think St. Croix needs a benevolent despot to take charge for a while. School repairs required, contractors hired, date set, - delivery of services with efficiency or workers dismissed. There is money somewhere in the budget for books. Locate it, purchase the books, delivery date set, and if not accomplished, contracts terminated along with the persons responsible."

"Now brother Malcolm", St. Croix doesn't have a Malcolm X at the helm. "The Virgin Islands are a territory of the United States, has an elected governor, and is under the Department of the Interior."

"Well then maybe the Department of the Interior needs to step in and say that a territory with a population of about 160,000 does not need 15 Senators. The ratio of people to Senators in the VI is absolutely outlandish along with their salaries."

"Malcolm, you're doing a critical analysis of the problems in St. Croix while I'm trying to impress you with our inventions. Why don't you go inside and view our Inventor's scrolls

Sojourner agreed to the suggestions and beckoned Malcolm to follow her as she gave Grant a parting bemused look.

The entrance of Inventor's Enclave resembled a two-sided conference room. There were inventions on the parquet floor, on marble, wooden, and metal stands and tables and some hanging from a ceiling draped and cushioned with silver tone velvet, ruffled, material. Miraculously, the large double doors that led into the entrance were unfettered. The two sidewalls however were covered with the listing of the residents of all races, in no particular order with dates of their inventions and when possible the patent number(s).

INVENTORS & THEIR INVENTIONS were inscribed in marble bas-relief.

Inventor	Invention/Product	Date/Patent #
Onesimus	Small Pox Inoculation (*fr. Africa*)	1721
Philip Emeagwali	World's Fastest Computer	1989
T. Grant	Golf Tee	12.12.1899
Thomas W. Stewart	Mop	6.11.1893
Paul L. Downing	Mailbox	10.27.1891
Elijah McCoy	Lubricating Cup	11.15.1895
W.A. Martin	Lock	7.23.18--
J. Thomas White	Lemon Squeezer	12.8.1893
J.W. Smith	Lawn Sprinkler	5.4.1897
Mary Walton	Smoke Stack Emission Deflector	1879/ USP#221,880
Mary Walton	Train Noise Reduction System	1881/ USP#237,422
W.B. Purvis	Fountain Pen	1.7.1890/ USP#419,065
W. A. Lovette	Advanced Printing Press	
W. F. Burr	Railway Switching Device	10.31.1899/ USP#636,197
William Barry	Postmarking & Canceling Machine	
J. W. Reed	Dough Kneader & Roller	9.2.1884
John Lee Love	Pencil Sharpener	11.23.1897
James Forten	Sailing Apparatus	1850
Jan Matzeliger	Automatic Shoe Making Machine	1883
John A. Johnson	Wrench	
Lydia O. Newman	Hair Brush	
Madame C.J. Walker	Hair Care Products	1905
Marjorie Joyner	Permanent Hair Weave Machine	11.27.1928/ USP#1,693,515
Madeline M. Turner	Fruit Press	1916
Michael C. Harvey	Lantern	8.19.1884
F. J. Loudin	Key Chain	1.9.1894
Sarah Boone	Ironing Board(*Improvements*)	12.30.1887
A. C. Richard	Insect Destroyer Gun	2.28.1899
Norbert Rillieux	Improved Sugar Making	12.10.1846

A.L. Cralle	Ice Cream Scooper	2.2.1897
J. Ricks	Horse Shoe	3.30.1885
Walter B. Purvis	Hand Stamp	2.27.1883
Robert F. Flemming, Jr.	Guitar	3.3.1886
Garrett A. Morgan	Gas Mask	10.13.1914
Brody & Surgwar	Folding Chair	6.11.1889
J.W. Winters	Fire Escape Ladder	5.7.1878
T. Marshall	Fire Extinguisher	10.26.1872
Alexander Miles	Elevator	10.11.1867
Lewis Latimer	Electric Lamp Bulb	3.21.1882
Willie Johnson	Eggbeater	2.5.1884
O. Dorsey	Door Knob & Door Stop	12.10.1878
Lawrence P. Ray	Dust Pan	8.3.1897
G. T. Sampson	Clothes Dryer	6.6.1862
Henry T. Sampson	Cellular Phone	7.6.1971
S.R. Scratton	Curtain Rod	11.30.1889
William S. Grant	Curtain Rod Support	8.4.1896
T. Elkins	Chamber Commode	1.3.1897
Charles Drew	Blood Plasma Bag	1945
A.P. Ashbourne	Biscuit Cutter	11.30.1878
L.R. Johnson	Bicycle Frame	10.10.1899
W. H. Richardson	Baby Buggy	6.18.1899
G. Cook	Auto Fishing Device	5.30.1899
Benjamin Banneker	Almanac	1791
Granville T. Woods	Auto Cut-off Switch	1.1.1839
Alice Parker	Heating Furnace	1918
Andrew Beard	Automatic Car Coupling Device	1897
Augustus Jackson	Ice Cream	1832
B.F. Jackson	Gas Burner	
C. B. Brook	Street Sweeper	1896
C.V. Richey	Fire Escape Bracket	12.28.1897/ USP#596,427
Frederick M. Jones	Ticket Dispensing Machine	6.27.1939/ USP#2163754
Frederick M. Jones	Starter Generator	7.12.1949/ USP#2475842
Frederick M. Jones	2-Cycle Gasoline Engine	11.28.1950/ USP#2523273

Frederick M. Jones	Portable X-Ray Machine	
Darryl Thomas	Cattle Roping Apparatus	
C.W. Allen	Self Leveling Table	11.1.1890/ USP#613,436
Bessie V. Griffin	Portable Receptacle	1951
D. McCree	Portable Fire Escape	11.11.1890/ USP#440,322
Philip Emeagwali	Accurate Weather Forecasting	1990
T. A. Carrington	Stove	7.25.1876
Madame C. J. Walker	Straightening Comb	1905
John W. Reed	Rolling Pin	1864
C.O. Bailiff	Shampoo Headrest	10.11.1898
M. A. Cherry	Tricycle	5.6.1886
Burridge & Marshman	Typewriter	4.7.1885
Edmond Berger	Spark Plug	2.2.1839
Granville T. Woods	Phone Transmitter	12.2.1884
Joseph Hunger Dickenson	Record Player Arm	1.8.1819
George W. Carver	Peanut Butter	1896
George W. Carver	Products from Peanuts (300); Sweet Potato (118) & Pecans (75)	1900-1943
Garrett Morgan	Automatic Traffic Signal	1923
Frederick M. Jones	Motor	6.27.1939
W.D. Davis	Riding Saddles	10.6.1895
Nathaniel Alexander	Folding Chair	7.7.1911
Patricia Bath	Laserphaco Probe (For Eye Care)	1986
Henry Blair	Seed Planter	10.14.1834
Charles Brooks	Improvement to Street Sweeper	3.17.1896
Marie & Albert Brown	Closed Circuit Television Security System	10.30.1922
George Crum	Potato Chip Inventor	1853
Mark Dean	IBM PC PS/2 Models 70 & 80	
Percy Lavon Julian	Glaucoma Medications & Foam to Extinguish Gas & Oil Fires	1953+
Joseph Lee	Bread Crumb Making	6.4.1895

Joseph Lee	Bread Crumb Making Machine	6.4.1895
Elijah McCoy	Locomotive Lubricator	4.1915
Carter G. Woodson	Negro History Week	2.1926
Alice Parker	Central Gas Heating System	1919
Sarah Goode	Improved Cabinet Bed System	7.14.1885/ USP#322177
J. B. Allen	Clothes Line Support	12.10.1895/ USP#551,105
A.P. Ashbourne	Refining Coconut Oil	7.27.1880/ USP#230,518
William Bailes	Ladder Scaffold-Support	8.5.1879/ USP#218,154
A.J. Beard	Rotary Engine	7.5.1892/ USP#478,271
J.H. Hunter	Portable Weighing Scales	11.3.1896
B. F. Jackson	Gas Burner	4.4.1899
A.F. Hilyer	Registers	10.14.1890/ USP#438,159
F. H. Harding	Extension Banquet Table	11.22.1898/ USP#614,468
C. J. Dorticus	Machine for Embossing Photo	4.16.1895/ USP#537,442
C. J. Dorticus	Photographic Print Wash	4.23.1895
J Forten	Sail Control	1850
W. R. Davis, Jr.	Library Table	9.24.1878/ USP#208,378
T.A. Carrington	Range	7.25.1876/ USP#180,323
Henry Blair	Corn & Cotton Planters	10.14.1834
L.C. Bailey	Folding Bed	7.18.1899/ USP#629,286
L. F. Brown	Bridle Bit	10.25.1892/ USP#484,994
Latimer & Brown	Water Closets for Railway Cars	2.10.1874/ USP#147,363
Latimer & Nichols	Electric Lamp	9.12.1881
Jan E. Matzeliger	Tack Separating Mechanism	3.25.1890
A. L. Lewis	Window Cleaner	9.27.1892
W. A. Lavalette	Printing Press	9.17.1878
A. Miles	Elevator	10.11.1887
H.H. Reynolds	Safety Gate for Bridges	10.7.1890/ USP#437,937
D.W. Shorter	Feed Rack	5.17.1887
S.E. Thomas	Pipe Connection	10.9.1888/
Snow & Johns	Linament	10.7.1890/ USP#437,728

J. Wormley	Life Saving Apparatus	5.24.1881/ USP#242,091
J. W. West	Wagon	10.18.1870/ USP#108,419
A. C. Richardson	Churn	2.17.1891/ USP#446,470
A. C. Richardson	Insect Destroyer	2.28.1899/ USP#620,362
W. B. Pruvis	Bag Fastener	4.25.1882/ USP#256,856
W. Purdy	Device for Sharpening Edged Tools	10.27.1896/ USP#570,337
L.A. Russell	Guard Attachment for Beds	8.13.1895/ USP#544,381
F. R. Perryman	Caterers' Tray Table	2.2.1892/ USP#468,038
S. E. Thomas	Pipe Connection	10.9.1888/ USP#390,821
A. P. Ashbourne	Process for Preparing Coconut for Domestic Use	6.1.1875/ USP#163,962
T. Elkins	Toilet	1897
Garnett A. Morgan	Gas Mask	1914
Granville T. Woods	Steam Boiler/Radiator	1884
Marie B. Brittan Brown	Security System	12.2.1969/ USP#3,482,037
Lydia Holmes	Wood Toys	11.14.1950/ USP#2,529,692

<u>Chapter Nine Glossary and Endnotes</u>

- *Romare Bearden (1911-1988):* Born in Charlotte, North Carolina. An educator, African- American master artist and world-renowned collagist.
- *Laura Davies:* Born in Coventry, England on October 5, 1963. She is an extremely talented professional golfer who has earned distinction within various US Golf Associations and poised to become a member of the LPGA Hall of Fame.
- *Eli Whitney (1765-1825):* Born in Westborough, Massachusetts of European-American heritage. An American inventor responsible for the infamous cotton gin that *"revolutionized"* the productivity and profitability of cotton production in America among other things. Some historians and writers have stated that he was an African American and he was not.

Chapter X

Writers and Poet's Pavilion

The sturdy canvas canopy was an eye soothing aquamarine, matching the cushions that covered the seat and back of the benches. A rack filled with pamphlets, pocketbooks and travel guides along with a beverage dispenser were sheltered from the sunrays by a roof and three sides made from woven tan raffia. A kiosk contained hi-tech glass framed maps, the kind where you press a button for your destination and colored lines indicate the many various routes, streets, lanes or trail lines that will take you there. Melodious tinkling of chimes swinging in time with a breeze weaved in and out and around about the rail station. Several yards away, pink and violet entwined flowers indicated the male and female comfort rooms. Every half hour a duet, soprano and alto, sang out the time and destination of the next cloud rail express.

An index finger pressed a button, the sound of a bottle sliding down a chute, and then the words, "Sure ain't 'Ripple' but it'll do until the real thing comes along." The pomegranate flavored spring water, chug a lugged to bottoms up. "Aahh, that was refreshing but it took a while for me to get used to this alcohol free stuff." He let forth a loud faked belch and his reddish beige colored face lit up in a sly grin as he watched the expression on his traveling companion's face.

"You ill-mannered, half Seminole, half Black, half-ass man, you're not on stage any more, you're up here in the heavenly pastures, and you still can't behave properly."

No longer dressed in her 'early bag lady' regalia, - instead of a bedraggled housedress and outlandish hat, rolled down socks and large sneakers, - she wore a square neck red tunic adorned with gold colored designs and well-fitted black stretch pants. Moms Mabley was one of the most successful entertainers of the black vaudeville stage, (*Chitlin' Circuit*) earning $10,000 a week at

Harlem's Apollo Theatre in the early '60's. She was billed as the funniest woman in the world.

"I don't know why I continue to travel with you. When we get to Pacifist's Paradise I'm going to see if Mahatma Gandhi or one of the Dalai Lamas can talk some piety into your soul."

"Some pie what? What kind of pie you talking about? Listen, now you listen to me, my soul and tongue has been reformed since I've been here. The air is so rarified, that I can't even *think* of a dirty joke or party joke, as the hinkty folks used to call them."

"Pi-et-ty, fool, I've been hanging out with poetry people such as Gwendolyn Brooks, Tillie Olsen, June Jordan and Lorraine Francis Joseph, but Mr. Sanford, why you say that your mind is purified? I remember just the other night at George Kirby's flat you were telling a story about Pinocchio's nose and a particular part of George President Bush's anatomy and what happens when lies are told."

"I don't remember any such story."

"Let me refresh your fading memory. You said that if Bush's third arm grew whenever he told a lie he could be at his Texas ranch and without leaving the house, use the White House facilities to relieve his kidneys."

"I remember no such words coming out of my mouth. I been purified but I can't stop my memory from remembering, Ripple wine, corrupt casino gambling and wild, willing, women, but be respectful now, because look who's coming our way."

"Good morning to my comedian friends", greeted Sojourner.

"As-Salaam Alaikum, my sister and brother."

"And a slam a lake um to you, brother, and a good morning to you, Madame Sojourner Truth."

192

Rising from the bench, Moms Mabley embraced Sojourner. "We are waiting for the cloud rail that is due in a few minutes. We're on our way to Pacifist's Paradise for a short visit and I'm trying to get Redd to clean up his language. Martin Luther King Jr. and Coretta Scott King along with Medgar Evers caught the earlier rail as we were arriving. Mahatma is holding one of his frequent weekend retreats."

Meanwhile the two men with their reddish brown hair and complexion engaged in jovial interchanges. Malcolm was known as "Detroit Red", having grown up in Michigan and Foxx was dubbed "Chicago Red" having been raised in Chicago. Redd Foxx wore his characteristic open collared light pink shirt a brown alpaca cardigan and loose fitting hounds tooth tan slacks.

"Our days when we were working in the speakeasy, I as a waiter and you as a dishwasher, are long gone. Just look at us", said Malcolm with that marvelous toothsome smile that practically covered the entire bottom of his face. The men gave one another that typical manly hug with shoulder pats.

"I must admit, coming here gave me a big break from the IRS. Remember they were hounding me in my sleep for money that I earned and they claimed. Listen to those songbirds singing to us, telling us, - 'here comes our ride'. We'll get together when we return." Redd Foxx hastened over to Moms Mabley and they made their way to the sleek, comfortable silver gray lightening fast train.

The rail train with its smooth and slick acceleration aptly fit the expression 'greased lightening', as it glided under the high cirrus and cirrostratus clouds. No exhaust so no pollution, silent as a rainbow and its radar equipment keeping flying creatures at bay. Malcolm and Sojourner watched in admiration for the few seconds that it was in sight.

A well-modulated poetic voice broke into their gaze, "Sojourner, I must be early or you late because our paths don't usually cross during our customary morning walks until we are past the transportation station."

"I am a bit late this mornin', Sister Gwen. Walking with brother Malik can be consuming. Ain't just a plain, natural stroll, oh no, you engage in conversation that is mighty consuming of your intellect 'cause you got to be aware of which philosophy he's coming from, - then I use more energy shaking this precious walking stick from Patrice Lumumba at Malcolm when he gets too rambunctious."

"But I'm sure Sister Sojourner that you won't object to spending time with Sister Brooks." Malcolm making a grandiose bowing gesture towards the poet pronounced, "Time spent with the first African-American to win the Pulitzer Prize for poetry, and has been awarded more than seventy-five honorary degrees from colleges and universities worldwide, and now hear this, - she was the Poet Laureate of Illinois in 1968, - is time well spent indeed."

The two women smiled as they exchanged unabashed looks.

Her hair cropped in a well-coifed Afro, her familiar black, heavy rimmed eye spectacles were replaced by stylish silver-rimmed designer glasses, her figure still trim and neat, appearing prim but graciously warm, Gwendolyn Brooks mused, "It's nice to hear the accolades but like those of us who started life Black and not rich, the racial prejudices and economic depravations should be remembered as part and parcel of achieving success. My father was the son of a runaway slave, and my mother gave up teaching for marriage and motherhood. Despite the conditions, they nurtured me mentally, emotionally and educationally. My dad provided a desk and bookshelves; my mother took me to meet Harlem Renaissance poets Langston Hughes and James Weldon Johnson."

Speaking aloud she said, "It's not often that I meet up with two of the Retreat's most revered inhabitants and I welcome the opportunity to share space that encircles the three of us."

194

"Since we are all moving in the direction of your home, Poet's Pavilion, let us tarry no longer."

In Malcolm's eyes mirth held its own as he digested the stylistic prose of his fellow walkers. He wordlessly joined pace with the women as they made their way toward the compound of bungalows that comprised the poet's residences. Nothing fancy, a rectangular plot housing natural mahogany clapboard buildings and in the typical retreat landscaping, a preponderance of flowering plants predominantly bird of paradise, poinsettia, heliconia, yellow and red ixora, jasmine and rambling pink roses.

Prior to reaching the courtyard of the pavilion Gwendolyn Brooks informed Malcolm and Sojourner that this morning, the group responsible for the 'Poets Pavilion Publication' would be holding their monthly meeting. She reminded them that the poets and writers were a very close-knit family who religiously praise and compliment one another.

In the courtyard of the Pavilion, a large orchid tree was vying for space that a pink poui tree had previously claimed. Eight members of the so-called editorial staff were perched, lounging, or seated on chairs to their peculiar liking. The chairs were assembled in an irregular, free flowing circle.

Claude McKay sat in a plaid cushioned wicker chair next to Gloria Anzuldua who lounged in a brown soft leather covered couch. Jamaican born McKay was a leading poet and novelist of the Harlem Renaissance and Gloria Anzuldua, a self-described "chicana dyke-feminist, tejana patlacha poet, writer, and cultural feminist", often shared their views on racial and cultural politics. McKay's poem 'If We Must Die' and Gloria's 'Borderlands/La Frontera' resonates with the spirit of facing racial and cultural differences in a radical revolutionary way.

Robert Hayden and Henry David Thoreau occupied Planters chairs. Essex Hemphill leaned forward from the edge of his overstuffed pale green twill arm chair and said to them, "With your arms crossed behind your heads and your feet crossed on the foot rests, you look like you're waiting for some slave to come along and pull off your boots and rub your feet, but don't worry it won't happen here. For the likes of me, I can't even understand why you're sitting in Planters chairs."

"Essex, you haven't lost a bit of your boldness or confrontational posture since you've been here. Relax a bit man. You're only 38 years young. I've been here since 1980, arrived at age 67. David here, well he arrived in 1862. Up here you can't get old before your time due to the rarified air, but take time to stop and smell the roses and all the other flowers in the Retreat."

Essex shrugged lightly and smiled softly in response to Hayden's words. Robert Hayden understood Hemphill's perspective on life. Essex, an African- American poet, activist, and performance artist expressed his feelings with hard, harsh, criticisms on issues of racism, sexism, homophobia, and heterosexism. A major theme in his writings was the disjunction between Black men and Black gay men. He also wrote about the realities of living as a Black, gay man with AIDS (*Acquired Immune Deficiency Syndrome*).

Emily Dickenson, Sylvia Plath and June Jordan's chairs formed an arc outside of the irregular circle of chairs. June was in a director's chair, Sylvia rested on a beige, leather office chair that revolved quite readily, and Emily was comfortably sprawled on a settee covered with rainbow colored spongy material.

The group of eight poets greeted the trio with pleasantries. Gloria Anzaldua invited them to join the group indicating to Sojourner to take the empty armchair. "Our brother Langston Hughes was supposed to be here but he had a previous engagement. We always have an odd number in the group so there will be no ties in the voting. Gwen will have to fill in for him if necessary."

Essex brought chairs for Malcolm and Gwendolyn. "Thank you brother", said Malcolm, "and tell me, how are the poets down below, the earth poets, confronting the establishment these days?

196

Any new versions of the 'Last Poets'? Anyone writing plays like Amiri Baraka's 'Slave Ship'?"

"Malcolm, that's a huge question. I must say that I am out of touch when it comes to who's who in the current generation of poets. But in my days on earth I appreciated the fact that artists, whether poets, illustrators, writers or photographers, had a deep sense of responsibility in terms of their creations being a bedrock for future generations", answered Sylvia. "I hope and trust that the valued artistry of past generations of poets has not been ignored or unknown to the present generation of poets and writers."

"Call me old fashioned", joined in Emily, "but last week I viewed a program featuring what I think was called 'Slam Poetry' and I simply question style versus substance."

Emily Dickinson was recognized as one of America's greatest poets after her death. Her persona those days was a far cry from the eccentric she was during her fifty-six years on earth. Born in Amherst, Massachusetts, in 1830 she hardly ever left home and was known as an eccentric recluse.

In her later years, she dressed in white, avoided strangers and her communication with friends was largely through notes and poems. Like Thoreau, she lived simply with austerity and intensity. When she died from Bright's Disease, an acute and chronic kidney condition, only seven of her poems were in print and anonymously. There was a period in her life when she wrote on the average a poem a day many of them containing philosophical and tragic dimensions. In the Retreat, Emily was a welcomed gad-about whose wardrobe would be the envy of the Project Runway models.

Today she was decked out in a knee- length botanical print linen-blend dress with a waist-defining belt and as for footwear, glamorous coffee colored leather sling backs with a two and a half stacked wedge heel.

"What do you mean Emily when you say you question style versus substance?"

"Oh, Gwen you know what I mean. I have no quarrel with poets revealing the harsh realities of life be it Black life, gay life, a miner's life or a drug addict's life. There are poets and rappers down there celebrating Black sexuality and Black dysfunction and the lyrics and the way they perform, I just didn't get the feeling of their work as being rooted in the uses of political power and social philosophy, which I believe to be the essence of the work of a poet. Their performances were more commanding than their poetry", was Emily's passionate response.

"Let me go back to Malcolm's general question about what's going on in the world of poetry. Let's start with 'Poetry Slam' - that's what it's called Emily, - I thoroughly enjoyed watching them. I wish that I could be there, I could out- perform the best of all them," bragged Essex. Noting the perplexed look on Sojourner's face, he continued. "Sojourner, Malcolm, Emily, all of you who aren't too familiar with Poetry Slam, it's a competition at which poets read or recite their poetry and on rare occasions other poets work, and their performances are judged on a numerical scale by members of the audience."

Gloria Anzaldua, looking especially attractive in a black bowler hat and a black, slinky tunic, pants and open jacket set that was complimented by a lengthy scarf that was gorgeous mix of forest green, purple, aqua and gold, added, "A couple of decades before my arrival in 2004, poetry slam was started in Chicago, and Marc Smith is credited with its origin. At a typical poetry slam members of the audience, or previously selected persons, act as judges for the event. After each poet performs the judges award a numeric score to that poem."

"Essex added, "The last one I watched was the first ever, **Women of the World Poetry Slam,** held in Detroit, Michigan, March 2008, and won by Andrea Gibson. There were twelve amazing women poets and they showed the earthly world the incredible power of performance poetry."

"What you mean, Essex, women only, aren't these slammin's open to all who think they can write and recite poetry?"

"Yes they are open to all and although it started in America slams or slammings as you call them, are held all over the world, Canada, Germany, Switzerland, France, Singapore, even Bosnia and Macedonia. Sojourner, there are different types of competition. In an "Open Slam", the most common type, all who wish to compete can enter. If there are too many for the allotted time, competitors are chosen at random from the sign up list. In an "Invitational Slam", only those invited compete. And a "Theme Slam", as the name implies, requires all performances conform to a specific theme with certain restrictions."

Henry David Thoreau entered the discussion. "I guess I can call myself an old-timer too. A large number of people know me as the Walden Pond poet, 'Walden' being my most popular work. I'm also considered a social philosopher and an environmentalist ahead of my time, but I was also engaged in intense political issues. But I raise the same questions as Emily, to what extent are these poets continuing the tradition of being political and social agitators to the establishment?"

"I don't think many people are familiar with your engagement in radical politics", offered Claude McKay, nodding with knit eyebrows in Henry's direction. "You were active in your defense of John Brown and one time filled in for Frederick Douglass at a convention. David, you were right alongside the fighting revolutionaries. Your most famous essay, *Resistance to Civil Government, (posthumous title) On The Duty Of Civil Disobedience,* speaks well to your political affinity. Frequently, the public doesn't recognize the true essence, talents, and messages of a poet or artist until after their death, our friend Emily Dickinson is an example."

"When we talk about the responsibilities of the poet are we not referring to one's philosophy of life that comes through in our work? As we upset the status quo, as we challenge other's sensibilities, we do so with integrity that requires a disciplined, dedicated work ethic", chimed in Sylvia.

"I don't know about the disciplined part, Sylvia, but I do know that I was dedicated to my writing. Born in Jamaica, West Indies, youngest of eleven children, at an early age I lived with an older brother who was a schoolteacher. I immigrated to the USA in 1912 and enrolled at Booker T. Washington's famous Tuskegee Institute and what a re-awakening. It was there that I encountered the stark, harsh, unadulterated realities of American racism. That formed the basis of much of my subsequent writings. I began writing poetry at age 10 and I wish they had Poetry Slam then." A jovial Claude called out, "Essex, let's you and I have a slam poetry contest and the publication board could be the judges."

The saucy, pertinent wit of Gloria Anzaldua came through as she spoke, "Listen up, folks, there is a wide, wide range of voices, cultural traditions, and styles in poetry slam. Some poets lean heavily on vocal delivery, some use the tradition of dub poetry, others use theatrical devices like shifting voices and tones, and then again, some use monotone. You will find poets using a format that includes tap-dancing or well-choreographed movements.

Reactions to poetry slams remind me very much of what some critics say of my work. In my writings in "Spanglish", a unique blend of eight languages, two variations of English and six of Spanish, it creates a daunting task for the non-bilingual reader to decipher the full meaning of the text. The reader feels frustrated and irritated. Well they are experiencing the emotions that I dealt with throughout my entire life as I struggle to reconcile language, cultural and racial differences. My writings and poetry slams are different forms of literary expressions. As the saying goes, 'don't criticize what you don't understand'."

200

"Well, Miz Gloria, I am not criticizing. This old woman from a distant place in time is desperately trying to understand this kind of poetry. You talk about 'dub' poetry and tap-dancing and shifting voices, - what's all that got to do with poetry?"

McKay explained, "Dub poetry is a rhythmic and political genre belonging to black and particular West Indian culture. There is a distinctive cadence and rhythm and style of speech, - sort of goes like this", -Claude gave a brief rendition of dub poetry accompanied by hand clapping and foot stomping to demonstrate the rhythmic beat.

"Show it off, McKay! Essex, I'm voting for Claude in the contest he proposed", taunted Robert Hayden. "Sister Sojourner, I can understand your dilemma about poetry slam. But you know about hip-hop from your visits with Tupac Shakur. Some poets use a delivery much like the hip-hop style. What has value today can lose its value later on down life's road. Should there be rules and regulations written in concrete that one must follow to be considered a poet? I certainly wouldn't agree to such an elitist idea. But I do hold certain criteria for the writer, whether it's poetry, prose, novels, fiction or non-fiction, and a responsibility to the public is one of them."

"Sojourner", continued Gloria, "piggy-backing off of Robert's words, a goal of poetry slam is to challenge the authority and audacity of anyone who claims to have absolute authority over literary value. What has value today can lose the important of its value and meaning over time. In slams, every poet is critiqued and everyone is at the mercy of the audience. In this sense, the audience can be likened to the establishment."

"Poetry slam definitely has a place in the world of poetry whether we up here in the lofty climate agree or disagree with its merits but someone on earth has an obligation to keep substance honorable. Let's get back to Malcolm's question about the 'Last Poets'" said June Jordan.

"Oh yeah", beamed Malcolm. "That's a group I will never forget. The original Last Poets was formed in 1968, on my birthday, May 19, at the former Mount Morris Park, at 124th Street and Fifth Avenue in New York City. It's now called Marcus Garvey Park."

"I always found the origin of their name to be very incisive. The name, Last Poets, is taken from a poem by the South African revolutionary poet, Keorapetse Kgositsile, who believed he was in the last era of poetry before guns would take over."

"Brother Robert," Malcolm intoned, "you were the master in experimenting with poetic form and the creation of different voices throughout your poetry. Your *Middle Passage* is a prime example. That poem speaks of the deep immortal human wish, the indomitable struggle for freedom, and Brother, I see that struggle as being timeless and will remain so until freedom truly comes to all."

"And that struggle for freedom was reflected in the messages that the Last Poets delivered as they played a major role in raising Black consciousness. Remember, they arose during the civil rights movement in the late '60's and it could be said that they were the Black Nationalist thread of the movement." Without missing a beat, June continued, "and I think it's important to name the original Last Poets. The group consisted of Felipe Luciano, Gylan Kain, and David Nelson."

"As an activist, performer and poet, and an angry and militant artist, I can relate to the bold, controversial, and highly politically charged poetry of the original Last Poets and the subsequent groups of Last Poets. At one point in time, the Last Poets was listed under the counter- intelligence program, founded by the former president, Richard 'Tricky Dick' Nixon."

"Essex Hemphill", began Sojourner, "son, you young enough to tell me a bit more about these Last Poets. Where are they today and what was their contribution to the world?"

202

Hemphill smiling broadly and handsome in his washed blue jeans and a dusty teal V-neck pull over, settled back in his seat, and gently fingered his Maori tiki before answering.

"Sister Sojourner, in the Last Poets we had poets who used rap and rhythms and percussions in their delivery of politically charged recitations. The groups were dedicated to black consciousness. They also introduced jazz and funk to their poetry. Okay, I know you are going to question funk and jazz in poetry."

"Humph", snorted Sojourner, "funk and jazz has been around long before you were born. I know about funk, -there's funky chicken, the blue funk, and plain ole smelly funk, but when it comes to poetry I like to hear just the poetry, not funk and jazz. Hear me, son?"

"Oh, I hear you loud and clear. I understand what you are saying. Sojourner, The Last Poets are recognized and considered to have almost single-handedly laid the groundwork for hip-hop. So, in their case they laid the groundwork for future generations and the social commentary aspects has not been lost on the rappers. The Last Poets recently had a resurgence of their work after a decline in the '70's. Some prominent musicians have produced albums uniting these famed pioneers of politically charged group poetry with current rap artists."

"Much obliged for that info, Essex. That hip-hop seems to have made a true impression on the music and literary scene. So are you Retreat poets hip-hopping and doing jazzing poetry?"

"Sojourner and Malcolm", said Gwendolyn, "It's sort of amusing and interesting, the type of activities that goes on up here among the poets. Occasionally we beam in on special events featuring poetry and scrutinize it, enjoy it, discuss its longevity, - but in the main, as innovative and creative as we are," and she gave a deferential smile, "we devise diversified activities that are both amusing and satisfying. For example, every month we publish a pamphlet titled, 'Nobody Asked Me But...'."

Claude McKay offered details. "Jimmy Cannon, born in 1910 and died in 1973, was a well known sports journalist who worked at the New York Daily News, wrote for The New York Post, New York Journal-American and King Features syndicate. He would often start his articles with, "Nobody asked me, but..." With respect, admiration, and apologies to Jimmy, we routinely publish a witty, philosophical, humorous, political, topical version of his column. Gwen is the editor."

"The poet congregation bestowed that honor, if you can call it that, on me as a birthday gift on June 7, 1999, my first year here, and I'd like to make it a revolving gift but there are no takers. However, I enjoy sparring with the writers about the entries. I think you'll find them ah, different, shall we say."

Sojourner stated that she was truly interested in reading the latest edition and McKay, fashionable in a lavender shirt with starched, pristine white cuffs and collar, dark lavender suspenders and beige tweed slacks, eagerly volunteered to get some liquid refreshments for the group and departed to the refreshment stand.

Gwendolyn went into Poet's Pavilion's office that resembled no office on earth. To begin with, everything was in place. Pens and pencils {minus the inventor's names), were in rainbow colors matching the embossed paper. Typewriters old fashioned and electric, computers, printing machines all in impeccable conditions were on Formica tables recessed in the sound proof, embossed rainbow walls. Cubicles of varying sizes, all equipped with velvet-covered roll around desk chairs with footrests and shelves loaded with paper clips, rubber bands, chewing gum, health bars, chilled bottled water, and tape recorders. Over one cubicle was a sign: **Editor-Gwendolyn Brooks** and on the desk was the latest edition of the monthly tabloid. The editor entered her cubicle collected the article and checked out her reflection in the floor length mirror on the wall. Satisfied with the style and fitting of her paisley Mother Hubbard dress and open toe sandals she returned to the group

204

Sojourner and Malcolm seated next to one another jointly began reading the papers Gwen had given to them.

Engraved black lettering was on re-cycled yellow papyrus:

Poets and Writers Monthly Tabloid

Page 1 of this edition was compiled by the following: Henry David Thoreau; Emily Dickinson; Sylvia Plath; Claude McKay. Comments from others have already been considered and no changes will be made, but feel free to offer comments or discuss our entries.

NOBODY ASKED ME BUT....

The United Nations Security Council's permanent members should be composed of countries, republics, Islands that have the best PEACE records, not those with the most military might.

With our bodies, we make passages thru life and no one can come thru that exact tunnel.

No human is an Island yet every human is an Island

Politicians should be barred from using the word 'honest'.

Wouldn't it be inspiring to have a National League of Intellects wherein teams would compete in intellectual games? There would be yearly tryouts and the selected competitors would receive million dollar contracts, (With the stipulation that half would be used to further intellectual development for grade school students) and wear uniforms with their names emblazoned across the backs of their blouses or shirts and established fan clubs would vigorously follow their teams.

Where does the pain go when it goes away?

American women spend millions of dollars and tons of time speaking out against genital mutilation in African and certain Middle East countries. Why isn't there a similar outcry against the bodily mutilation among women in the USA- breast reductions, breast addition, nose, ears and eyes re-shaped, liposuction, botex squeezed into every and any wrinkle or hollow, belly tucks, feet re-constructed - with the exception of health reasons, women, why do you do it?

I have an explanation for the Mona Lisa smile: Mona Lisa was a clairvoyant. She was looking into the 21st century in America and Dubya Bush was president. Her smile was in response to his policies and behaviors that she thought were a joke. The quizzical look is in response to her questioning, 'How can the Congress, voters and his family let him get away with his antics?"

After reading the first page Sojourner with a smile and quirked eyebrows, turned to Gwen and questioned, "Now tell me a bit more about these sayings we reading. Is this some new form of poetry or prose?"

"Whatever it is, I sure like the one about Mona Lisa. What manner of man or woman, -in this heavenly pavilion, -was so blessed with insightful opinion -", rhymed Malcolm with a roguish grin.

Slowly shaking her head from side to side, Gwen gave him an amused smile and explained, "Like I was saying, the poets want a diversion from their poetry and prose of yester-year. They come up with one- liner and /or brief statements that capture an essence of a particular aspect of life.

Malcolm immediately began to turn to page two. Sojourner held down the page saying to him, "I want to continue too but give me a little time to digest the first page. I 'specially like the one about our bodies making passages. Imagine a space of one's own, the cosmos at work. And it sure is true about honesty and politicians. What do you think of the writin's, brudder?

"I think the poets got a good thing going. I know it encourages lots of spirited discussions among them. I'm eager to read on."

Sojourner's gaze lingered on the pamphlet then she made several dabs at the page before turning it over.

Page 2 of **Poets and Writers Monthly Tabloid** was compiled by Essex Hemphill; June Jordan; Gloria Anzaldua; Robert Hayden. The fact that all the poets for this segment are non-Caucasian was serendipitous. The final selections of entries are the results of debates; rolling the dice; drawing straws and tradeoffs. We are united behind our choices and love them all.

Debates and definitions of racism would be more meaningful if the fact was acknowledged that RACE is a social construct, not a scientific biological fact. Ergo, Tiger Woods and Barack Obama could legitimately defy racial definitions and declare themselves social constructs.

Surf and turf in the ghetto translates to sardines and meatballs.

Is it true of golfers, the longer the golf drive, the shorter the sex drive?

With growing numbers of students who do not know the differences between a city and a state, a country and a continent, it's time to re-instate plain old geography in the curriculum.

What is the justification for the exorbitant salaries offered young male athletes in basketball, football, and baseball? Million dollar contracts for having exceptional athletic genes – outlandish.

There should be a limit to the number of Christmas gifts that children receive and that number is THREE. There were three wise men and each brought one gift to the baby Jesus. That sets precedence for gift -giving within a religious framework.

When people say, "I can't find words to express my feelings", they are saying that they have a limited vocabulary.

Angela Davis should be hired to design a rehabilitation program for the prison population to offset the corrupt Industrial Prison Complex; and at the same time there should be changes made regarding time served for certain violations of the law and equally important there should be educational /vocational programs instituted to prevent the need to incarcerate so many young men and women.

Elementary schools throughout the nation should have a mandate to teach Chinese and Arabic. Chinese will soon be one of the leading languages in the world and with the Middle East becoming more and more influential our students will be prepared to face the world linguistically.

Throughout the reading Malcolm and Sojourner smiled, frowned, chuckled, uttered ahh's; and um humph's. Gwen looked expectantly at the twosome as they completed the monthly print out. Malcolm, with his wide and a playful grin commented, "Sister Gwen, power to the poets for two pages of philosophy, education, sports and politics and anatomy."

Sojourner turned toward her companion, eyed him with scrutiny, gnarled hands tapping that walking stick and in her sonorous voice opined, "Brudder, these words, sayings, opinions and thoughts from our heavenly poetic friends are gut- level expressions of deeds and misdeeds of humankind and bountiful prophecies for the future." Turning toward Claude, Gloria, Emily and the others she

208

questioned, "Do you consider yourselves philosophers, politicians, griots, satirists, - in poet's clothing?"

June Jordan's white buffalo dangle earrings, a gift from fellow writer Gertrude Simmons Bonnin, swung noticeably in keeping with June's response. "As a poet/writer/social activist, speaking and writing social commentary were part and parcel of my daily life. Yes, Sojourner, I would say that we are all of the above as we discourse about many of today's values."

"Emily, you and David had a similar outlook when it comes to material values. Many of the young folk today follow a script that says, 'If it sells, produce it and to hell with consequences.' I am not wholesale condemning the earth poets and writers. We can rejoice and take splendid comfort in knowing that poets Sonia Sanchez, Adrienne Rich, Judy Grahn, Mari Evans, Chrystos, Lucille Clifton, to name several, are carrying on our traditions."

"Listen to that list, all women. We have some outstanding male poets still on earth. What's a word that means the opposite of macho-ism, male supremacy, sexism? How about 'female-ism, meaning female superiority and male inferiority? Can I accuse you of practicing 'female-ism'?" Essex Hemphill questioned as he stood up.

The great chronicler of the Afro-American experience, Robert Hayden spoke up, "Essex, Essex, of course there are male poets in action on earth, lots of them. I can't say for sure how many of them fit in the old tradition that we are talking about. Now there's Michael S. Harper from Brooklyn, New York, was poet laureate for Rhode Island from 1988 to 1993 and might I add", and Hayden puffed up his upper body, "that Michael Harper says that his sense of history is indebted to yours truly, Robert Hayden."

"Hear, hear, all compliments to Mr. Robert Hayden", cajoled Gloria Anzaldua.

Sylvia Plath in a dark red sleeveless belted shirt dress with princess seams and a skirt full of swingy pleats, spun around on her office chair saying, "Of course there are male poets out there as cultural preservers and political voices. There's Nathaniel Mackey, considered a master of rhythmic poetry. He won the 2006 National Book Award for Poetry, which came as a surprise since the award is rarely given for avant-garde poetry. Then there is the great works of the recently departed August Wilson. Speaking of playwrights, he was a genius, a la Amiri Baraka."

"Getting back to the Publication" said Sojourner, "I'm intrigued by the breadth of topics covered, that's why I asked if poets were griots, philosophers, and social commentators."

"You can add sports analysts to the list," said Malcolm. When did the poets become so intrigued with the sporting world?"

"Many of the athletes from the Arena stop by and they usually exaggerate their accomplishments or brag about how much greater they were than today's crop of hormone, steroid -fed athletes with all their super hi-tech equipment and outrageous salaries. And that George Grant, he's a true golfing addict", answered Claude McKay. "I asked him how true was the saying, 'the longer the golf drive the shorter the sex drive' since he was a golfer. He skirted the question by saying, that those big hitters at the Buccaneer, like Jeff Lee and Luis Belardo and on the distaff side, Pam Kantowski, Bernice Cole and Diane Burns, would definitely know the answer."

Gwen countered, "Now I may be the editor, but I am not accountable for all that is printed. But Malcolm, it's as I told you, the poets are engaged in writings that are atypical to their previous styles. What I definitely know about sports is the fact that if poetry paid off like home runs I would be a multi-millionaire."

A chorus of handclaps followed Gwen's remark. June Jordan sitting upright in her director's chair joined in, "When it comes to royalties, and making money, autobiographies by teenagers are big

210

sellers. Now just imagine that, - how in the universe can a teenager write an autobiography, - it should be called a half biography or a three-quarter biography. And there are all sorts of 'How To Books', plus the current wave of what they call 'Urban Novels', those are the money -making books."

Sylvia Plath addressed June, "To emphasize your point June, my autobiographical novel, The Bell Jar, is more popular than my poems, yet I believe my poems were much more reflective of my literary talents."

"I consider your talent to be brilliant, but I think it was the dramatization of the stereotyping of women's roles in the 1950's and the awareness of the fact that a woman's gifts and ambitions greatly exceeded the available options, that made The Bell Jar so appealing. It was a boon to the women's social movement," June responded.

Emily gazed at the group of poets then directed her comments to Sojourner and Malcolm, "Understand, we have done our poetic duty to the world and intend to relax and have a little fun with the written word."

"Sister Emily,, I just love Sister Gwen's Annie Allen and Maud Martha. Annie Allen gave our Editor Brooks the Pulitzer Prize for poetry and that was the first ever given to an African-American. I'm used to poetry that rhymes or if it prefers not to rhyme, den I like to read pleasant words that gives you a good feeling that you can carry through the day."

"In that case, Sister Sojourner, stay away from those urban fiction readings", were Claude's comments and Robert provided the Amen corner, " Yes, brother, yes indeed."

"I know it's because of the money and an audience ready to devour multiple depictions of, - how shall I describe it - steamy, juicy, hot sex; salacious seductions, rough, tough but smooth talking knife toting, gun packing hustlers; two timing men and women; dark secrets; supremely sexy and disgustingly devoted women; and I must not leave out the promiscuous preachers and the alluring gay guys. I have to question its overall value, I *just have* to." June tugged at the seam of her navy pinstriped, wide leg twill pants that blended with her azure jersey scoop neck top, and ran her fingers rapidly through her mixed gray, short-cropped hair.

Sylvia rested her hand over June's and patted it lovingly. "June, we cannot directly alter or interfere with the current generation's thoughts or behaviors. I know we left them solid literary roadmaps. We did our work and now we can appreciate the freedom from diseases of our bodies and minds. We were of different generations, our writings were very meaningful to some, unknown to others, and others could care less. Our works have been and will be valuable to generations to come. Similarly, urban fiction has its place in certain sectors on earth. Don't fret, let youth explore and experiment with all phases of literature in ways that are known to their generation."

Gwen closely observed her friends. She intuitively understood their angst. "My dear friends we all know that our time for writing poetry for the people is over. Our contributions will be available for generations to come. However, I thoroughly enjoy the way our monthly tabloid stimulates discussion and it's a rather new genre of expression for us. I joined this community on December 3, 2000, at age 83 and I believed then as I do now, to create 'bigness' you don't have to create an epic. 'Bigness can be found in a little haiku, five syllables, or seven syllables'."

Malcolm rose from his seat and approached Gwen with outstretched arms. His brotherly embrace was a spontaneously and warm response to her words and very being. "Sister Brooks, I find those comments, passages, homilies, and platitudes intriguing and refreshing, - makes want to try my hand at this type of literature. Can I summit some entries?"

His companion answered, "Malcolm, you have written and delivered enough fiery words and speeches that ignited a nation to

212

action. All you got to do is send in some of your responses to questions from your audience."

"Give us an example", said the editor- in- chief."

"Listen up" said Sojourner with a wholesome grin on her broad boned African features. "I recall this one. When 'Negroes' would brag about being born in America and therefore as Americans they had as much rights as any other American. Well, mam, brudder Malcolm's response was, 'If a cat has kittens in an oven that don't make them biscuits'."

"Malcolm X", said Gwen laughing along with the others, "you put together some of your gut retching homilies and statements and I'll give them to the poets in charge of next month's tabloid and they can be the judges.

Pleased with the response he gave a mock bow from the waist, saying, "Thank you Editor- in- chief, Brooks, your graciousness is exceeded only by your poetic excellence." His words were followed with a stream of verbal jabs from the poets, "His gift of gab at work" "Listen to the master of flattery." "The man was born with a gilded tongue."

At this point Sojourner declaring that she would like a copy of the paper, majestically rose from her arm chair and with that gift from Lumumba, beckoned her companion that it was parting time. "Now you all come back soon" called out Gloria. "It's always a muy splendorific experiencia"

"Hasta la vista", the duo said as a duet, as they departed.

<u>Chapter Ten Glossary and Endnotes</u>

- *Ripple:* The name of a cheap wine.
- *Chitlin' Circuit:* The name given the vaudeville circuit for African American performers during the 1920' and 1930's. There were routine places and theatres throughout the states that African American (*Black*) performers and entertainers were regularly booked for shows.
- *Botex:* A term related to "botox"- the nickname for FDA-approved *botulinum toxin* a most poisonous neurotoxic protein used for muscle spasms and cosmetic treatments.
- *Tillie Olsen (1912-2007):* American writer associated with the political turmoil of the 1930's first generation of American feminists. Olsen is best known for her poetic and wrenching novella, "<u>Tell Me a Riddle.</u>"
- *George Kirby (1923-1995):* African American comedian from Chicago and one of the first to appeal to a White and Black audiences. An excellent impressionist- targeting both Black and White popular personalities.
- *Medgar Evers (1925-1963):* African American civil rights activist from Mississippi who was murdered by Byron La Beckwith, a member of the Ku Klux Klan. Evers' death and the acquittal of Beckwith led to an outpouring of public protest. Thirty years after two previous trials that failed to convict Beckwith a new trial was held, he was convicted and imprisoned and died in prison.
- *Judy Grahn:* Born July 28, 1940 in Chicago, Illinois. She is an internationally known poet, woman-centered cultural theorist, co-founder of lesbian-feminism, and early contributor to literature of women's spirituality. She was a member of the Gay women's Liberation, the first lesbian feminist collective on the west coast founded around 1969.

  Angela Davis: Born January 26, 1944 in Birmingham, Alabama. An African American political activist currently a graduate studies Professor of History of Consciousness and Presidential Chair at the University of California, Santa Cruz. She works for racial and gender equality, gay rights and prison abolition. She is an extremely popular national and international public speaker and founder of grassroots prison industrial complex abolition organizations. Davis received nationwide notoriety in the '70's when she fled underground and was the subject of an intense manhunt, and considered by the FBI as their "most wanted" criminal. She was eventually arrested, tried and then acquitted in one of the nation's most famous trials in recent history.

State of the World Address

Sojourner stood, at her station in front of the dais, - solemnly, silent, serene and scrutinizing. The carved animal heads on her walking stick appeared to be on alert as she tightened and released the misshapen fingers of her right hand around the head of her stick. Her partner, Malcolm, resplendent in his blue suit and skinny red tie, (*his 'burning suit'*) was busy greeting guests from the stage, but tactfully analyzing his audience. The Retreat' s famed duo, were watching in an unobtrusive manner the east rear section of the amphitheatre. This was reserved for the Ancient Ancestors. Their arrival was the signal for the evening activities to begin.

No one ever asked, 'When do the festivities begin?', because all were aware of the answer, 'It begins when it starts and it starts with the arrival of the Ancient Ancestors.'

Amidst the light clamor and conviviality among the inhabitants of Revolutionary's Retreat and their neighbors, an imperceptible hush came over the theatre. Sure enough, a cloud mobile had landed adjacent to the reserved area. Six ancestral guests that were selected by their companions from their royal habitat emerged and took their seats. This dignified group consisted of:

Hatshepsut, a 15th century B.C. (*d.1458 B.C.*) ruler of Khamit (*Ancient Egypt*) during the infamous 18th dynastic period marveled for her prolific architectural monuments and militaristic efficiencies as one of the first female rulers- PerAa (pharaoh)- to govern this ancient nation who strengthened trade disturbed by Asiatic invasions and restored alliances with Punt, Kush, Nubia (*Contemporary Somalia, Ethiopia, Eritrea, Tigre and Sudan*) and others;

Makeda, a 10th century B.C. leader and resource-rich strategist known as "Queen of Sheba" who in Ethiopian legend became the wife of King Solomon and founder of the first royal line of the kingdom of Sheba/Saba in

217

southwest Arabia which has transcended to contemporary Ethiopian Orthodox religion and its' leaders;

Nzinga, a 16th to 17th century A.D. (*c.1583-1663*) warrior queen and military leader of Kimbundu—the united kingdoms of Ndongo and Matamba (*Contemporary Angola*) who during her reign no Africans were kidnapped or taken into slavery by the Portuguese;

Yaa Asantewaa, a 19th to 20th century A.D. (*c.1840-1921*) Queen Mother of Ejisu of the Ashanti Confederacy (*Contemporary Ghana)* and legendary freedom fighter and warrior leader of the historic Ashanti Rebellion against British colonial rule in 1900;

Dahia Al-Kahina, a 7th century A.D. (c.610-694) military and religious leader, known as a seeress and warrior queen who led indigenous military forces of the Berber ethnic nations of northwest Africa (*Contemporary Mauritania & Morocco*) against forced arabization; and

Askia Mohammad aka Muhammad Toure or Askia The Great, a 15th to 16th century A.D. leader (*c.1442-1538*) and Soninke king of the Songhai Empire, who developed and ruled an empire into one of the largest countries in West African history.

In recognition of the ancestors being seated, Sojourner rapped her stick sharply three times on the parquet stage floor. The audience ceased their chatter and began settling in the spacious, cushioned, recliner style seats. Looking regal in her customary full sleeve, full skirt dress and embroidered white shawl Sojourner re-adjusted her steel-rimmed glasses, lightly fingered her new bonnet with the black, red, and yellow trim, and in her sonorous tones addressed the heavenly people.

"This annual gathering, featuring the State of the World Address, for which you have all been waiting for wid much anticipation, no longer has a waiting period. With humility and respect for godliness, I hereby declare the opening of this annual conference. May our celebration seep wid compassion and intellect.

There is so much trouble, turmoil, tragedy, and turbulence between and among humankind, nature and the cosmos that this evening's activities will be replenishing, a welcoming balm as well as a restorative and soulful elixir."

In silent communication with Sojourner, Malcolm picked up a silver urn, made his way to center stage, and began pouring libations. Sojourner intoned words of prayer in a tongue unknown to others but the ancestors nodded emphatically. At the conclusion of the libations, Sojourner announced that at this time homage in dance form would be paid to the Ancestors, those present in the flesh and those present in spirit.

Stage lights were lowered, colorful strobe lights flashed rhythmically and Katherine Dunham, called the Matriarch and Queen Mother of Black dance, and in the 20th century had one of the most successful careers in American and European theatre, made a swirling entrance from the right side of the floor. Immediately following from the left side slithered Pearl Primus, Trinidadian born choreographer and anthropologist who immigrated to the United States as a toddler. The two dancers clad in flowing white costumes and accompanied by drummers performed a traditional dance of communication and sensual ancestral honor, the Bamboula, to the thrilling enjoyment and satisfaction of all.

Then the drummers began telling a story. Their powerful beats had the drumheads screaming with pleasure for mercy. In their reserved section, the Ancestors clapped, swayed, and nodded in appreciation. Askia's illustrious robes swayed in time with his vigorous clapping. The ritual dance struck a familiar chord in their being. The Retreat folks cheered, and vocally expressed their extreme pleasure.

Redd Fox keenly observed that the Ancestors were not vocal. Nudging Moms Mabley he said, "Are the ancestors mummified to the extent that they don't talk?"

"Redd, they use non-verbal communication whenever they leave their premises." "Nonverbal? You mean they talk without using verbs? Like, I home instead of I'm going home," he jested.

Moms totally ignored him except to remind him that Sojourner did not tolerate folks talking during performances and please do not let her have to tap that stick and rivet her eyes in our direction.

Native American musicians, drummers, singers, dancers and the flute players the wind riders followed the drummers. The wind riders are those who excel on the flute because they can transform 'wind' into magical flute music. Rituals dedicated to their Native American ancestors were performed for one half hour. The Native American ensemble filled the room and the surrounding area into a virtual reality of sounds of nature.

By now, the listeners were near intoxication from the images, sounds, vibes, and energies of the performances. Incredible animation and gestures of the Ancestors clearly expressed their appreciation and enjoyment. Sojourner waited courteously for the vibrations to sink and settle. Approximately thirty seconds later she announced, "The first lady of song will now preside."

Resplendent in a mink mufti colored satin trim skirt suit, Ella Fitzgerald appeared at center stage, radiating warmth, graciousness, and gentility. Smooth as satin the opening lines,
> *"I am weak but thou art strong,*
> *Jesus keep me from all wrong,*
> *I'll be satisfied as long,*
> *as I walk, let me walk close to thee",*

…with a rollicking, rhythmic, gospel beat captivated every one. Ella, with keyboard, piano, drums, and percussions as backups, intoned the gospel, *"Just a Closer Walk with Thee"*, into a

220

mesmerizing, rejoicing, rendition. When she hit the concluded lines with her inimitable mellow, melodious softened tempo,
"...daily walking close to thee,
let it be dear Lord let it be,
let it be dear Lord, let it be",

She had all present in the palms of her hands.

Malcolm gave Sojourner a knowing look and she nodded in agreement. During the planning of the festivities, Sojourner had wanted to sing a gospel. Malcolm had explained that this was not a revival meeting, nor an occasion wherein Sojourner had to be persuasive and lead followers with her entrancing vocalizing. As an itinerant Pentecostal preacher, she included singing along with her preaching to the public. Her singing voice was powerful, with a deep resonance that could bring chills or warmth to her listeners. Malcolm and Sojourner had agreed that the opening ceremonies should include Ella Fitzgerald and Sojourner would be reserved for the closing.

Sister Ella beaming with appreciation, took a sip of water, delicately patted her brow with a handkerchief, and slipped into, '*A Tisket a Tasket, a green and yellow basket*', one of her all time huge hits in the '50's. Her trio of songs ended with the ballad, '*Oh, Lady Be Good*', a song that established her jazz image. Ending with a breakneck scat solo, she and her heavenly audience shared unlimited joy.

Ella and her musicians received a standing ovation and this time ululating came from the Ancient Ancestors Hatshepsut, Kahina, Nzinga, Queen of Sheba, Yaa Asantewaa as Askia Mohammad vigorously stomped his feet.

Satisfaction and happiness was everywhere and Sojourner and Malcolm were emotionally and mentally ready to begin their evening's challenges. The audience, refreshed with the beverages galore, relaxed in readiness for the opening remarks from Brother Malcolm. Sojourner with her walking stick motioned an already silent audience for silence as El-Hajj Malik El-Shabazz strode to the podium.

Although this celebration occurred yearly, Brother Malcolm always felt a nostalgic rush. The moment brought back floods of memories, -standing before audiences of collegiate, religious, rank and file, middle class, affiliations -knowing that FBI agents, agents provocateurs were planted throughout the crowds, - and how he adeptly addressed them and then skillfully fielded all questions, most of which came from the depths of hostility, wariness, fear, ignorance and resentment. Malcolm relished in these memories also rejoiced in the fact that here in the Retreat he was received with love, understanding and compassion.

"As-salaam Alaikum. Sisters and brothers all, -you know you **have** been **welcomed** by the excellent entertainers, aheh, most of whom were women. Sister Sojourner, next year we will have to remedy that, that is, balance the number of male and female presenters."

"We are in the process of remedying it right now, this evening. For the past umpteen years, it's been imbalanced, so wimmin have a heap of number of years to catch up so tonight is a good starting time."

Malcolm grinned. "Thank you sister for keeping us on track and I know you will do so throughout the evening. I am proud of the contributions women have made. I'm for giving them all the leeway possible. They've made a greater contribution than many men."

He paused for a moment, readjusted his eyeglasses with the horn rimmed top and rim less bottoms. The special magnetic charm that characterized Malcolm radiated. "Tonight's main menu, State of the Union and World Address, will follow the familiar format, that of opening remarks by your hosts, followed by questions and responses that will reflect the integration of the relationship among and between the forces of nature, the nature of humankind, the

222

scientific explanation for being and the force fields of the spirit world.

Our time gazers give us firmament dwellers a distinct advantage in knowing all that takes place worldwide, both in terms of the real story and the secret plot. You know what I mean by those terms. Well the story they show you on television and tell you on the radio and newspapers, is supposed to be the real McCoy, the real truth. They want you to believe that you can grow real hair and use toothpaste that will make you look younger and be more attractive sexually. The secret plot is that they are selling baloney dressed up like sirloin steak and the gullible public buys it and swallows it. In actuality that is the real McCoy, making you believe the hype and consume and consume until you need another product to counteract the ills brought on by the former product." (*laughter from the audience*) "Have you ever listened to the ads on TV concerning medicines or treatments for your ailments? They will name a product and tell you what it is designed to heal or cure. Then they list the possible side effects in a rapid, slightly lower voice,' *side effects may include, nausea, nose bleeds, diarrhea, constipation, blurred vision, increased heart rate and in rare occasions, death.*' The side effects sound worse than the ailment. Those pharmaceutical companies are hype masters, masters of deceit and make millions, no billions in the process.

"The earth public, without the benefit of the Time Gazer, isn't cognizant of the wheeling and dealing, the conniving and chicanery that goes on behind the scenes. This evening as Sister Sojourner and I respond to your queries we will do so from the advantage of knowing - to some extent because no one knows it all - knowing the mendacity that is used to maintain a status quo that keeps the rich on top, the so-called middle class 'going round and round in circles getting nowhere very fast', as the song goes, and the so called lower classes living a Sisyphus* existence.

We are all quite aware of the complexities of the problems on a global level. And we are quite aware of the fact that there are reasonable answers to these problems. The logical question is, why

223

aren't they being applied? An over simplified answer is, because to do so would deregulate the status quo. But tonight my friends in the process of analyzing the problems I foresee an extremely exhilarating interchange. Now, Sister Sojourner, the podium is yours."

"Thank you, my Brother. As you all know, I came from the land of slavery and I shed them shackles, shed my given name, Isabelle Baumfree, and took on a God given name, one that described me well. I traveled the country speaking, preaching, and living the truth. Both Malcolm and I had similar thoughts in getting rid of our slave names. We also overcame hurdles and obstacles that made us seem fearless and therefore peculiar. That peculiarity propelled us to this stage tonight. We think outside of the prescribed mode of thinking that the masters wanted us to prescribe to.

The world problems today, the homeless, the hungry, one country invading another, wars, people killing and torturing their own kinfolks and then we have all the victims of nature that is victims of Katrina and other hurricanes, victims of earthquakes and cyclones in Myanmar and China and the monsoons in India, they are all victims of nature living out its natural existence, - rumblings, tumbling and belching deep in the earth resulting in eruptions and explosions and climatic changes, - water seeking its own level, winds exercising their power - and humankind unable to escape the paths of nature. Well, chillun's the questions are, could these problems be prevented? Who is responsible for solving these problems now that they are present?

Each generation seems to think that calamities are unique to their generation. Back in 1842 when I was with the Millerites, they lamented the world's conditions -earthquakes in the American mid-west; re-occurring terrible storms and shipwrecks; starvation in Scotland; hard living conditions in many states; the federal government's lack of money; the war in China contributing to great losses of life. Today's generation has to deal with similar calamities. This evening we are here to examine age-old problems in a new era. So let the questions begin."

224

Sojourner finished with a soul-satisfying smile. Malcolm joined her and they acknowledged the audiences' applause.

Eli Whitney, thinking about his New England climate and the possibility of it having Florida like temperatures stood up. Sojourner acknowledged him. "Global warming is a hot topic today. How much of all the palaver is hype and how much is truth, Sojourner?"

"The hype is mingled with truth, Eli, like it always is. Sure, there are climatic changes. There always have been and always will be. Think of all the geographic changes that have taken place since the beginning of time. Remember, at one time all the continents were joined forming a single super continent. A German meteorologist, named Wegener, called it Pangaea, Greek for "all lands." So there must have been powerful, masterful changes of all kinds - climatic, oceanic, and volcanic - to have a super continent change into six or seven landmasses, if you count Antarctica. Humans think they can control the weather. They can interfere wid it but humans cannot prevent natural, God directed changes. All the explanations about how and why these climatic changes are happening, and warnings and who's to blame and how we can slow it down, is all a part of the scheme to keep them, under control. They do a good job of making the everyday people think that those in power are truly powerful and care about protecting them."

"Amen sister, teach!" Malcolm joined the discussion. "Let me point out to you that it was some 18,000 years ago that the height of the ice age was experienced. Since that time, a series of radical changes in climate has taken place. Over the past 22 millennia a model of global temperature changes has been established and it is based on variations in the oxygen content of water in the ice cones of Greenland."

Ida B. Wells stood up with raised arm that was an indication of a need to interrupt the speaker. "Keep it simple El-Hajj Malik El-Shabazz, keep it simple."

"Thank you Sister Ida. Let me say that to understand the future of the climate you must study clues from the past. And it is quite possible that the conditions of the earth at the height of the ice age, some 18,000 years ago as I said, will return some day. Do you know that according to the climatologists, - I guess that's what you would call those persons who study the history of the earth, - a drop in global average temperatures of only 4 degrees fahrenheit could initiate a new ice age. New York City would lie under an ice sheet and you could walk from England to France.

All of this is simply to say that yes, certainly climatic changes are taking place and yes, we need to be aware of such in the same manner that we should be aware of the politics associate with it. Does human kind contribute to these climatic changes? Of course they do but to what extent? And can we halt or change nature's life path? We can be told that hair sprays and deodorant sprays pollute the air but what about those testing of nuclear weapons and rockets to the moon. Do they use non-polluting explosives? You see, politicians, presidents, Prime Ministers and the likes have a way of making you think that you are the criminal, you are polluting the environment and causing global warming and they are there to protect you. They want you to believe that the laws they put out are there to save you from harm when in actuality it's to keep them secure in their positions."

Ella Baker rose and asked, "It is true that in the far, far distant past the geographic and geological conditions were vastly different, but how helpful or destructive has man's role been in these current changes?"

"Fundi", began Sojourner, "I truly do not know the specifics of the customs, habits and behaviors of humankind billions of years ago, but I would wager that with their simplified way of living, there wasn't much pollution distributed. But listen here sisters and brothers. Today's global warming in some respects could have started eons ago. You all are familiar with this song I am about to sing. Sojourner, glad for the opportunity to sing let forth with her with her customary power and pathos:

226

'Ezikiel saw the wheels,
Way up in deh middle of deh air,
Ezikiel saw deh wheels,
turning in deh middle of deh air,
Oh, deh big wheel run on faith
and deh little wheel run by the grace of God,
A wheel in a wheel,
turning in deh middle of deh air,
Way up in deh middle of deh air'.

Malcolm moved to the side of the stage and with a slight upturn at the corners of his mouth watched the audience intently. He had heard Sojourner's version of chariots and global warming and was curious about the reception she would receive.

"Now as you know the wheels were the chariots, the burning chariots in the name of Jesus. Over time wid modern technology making improvements, improved modes of transportation happened. Those chariots were the forerunners of UFO's! Yes, chilluns, they need to stop calling them UFO's and start calling them IFO's because they have been identified. They are the mode of transportation for the so-called aliens. Now these discs or flying saucers or space ships that the aliens been flying around in for so many years certainly give off a heap of heat, and that contributes mightily to global warming."

There was a swell of murmurs, arched eyebrows, and looks of astonishment among the audience. Walter Rodney managed to be recognized and using the microphone that was on the armrest of each chair, spoke out.

"I know a lot of you may think that what Sister Sojourner has said is farfetched, but not so. Are there other beings inhabiting the world? Yes. There are those who know full well of the landing of the spacecraft in Roswell, New Mexico in 1947 and the acknowledgement of the capture of an alien body. There are eyewitnesses living today that can account for the landing of that saucer. And who knows what the military did with that little

227

creature they carted away from his spacecraft. The United States and other world power nations are not ready to deal with outer space beings so they con the public into believing what Malcolm referred to as a cover story. There are many factors that contribute to global warming, but as our hosts have explained, global warming is real, it has a geological and geographical past, it can and will affect our lives in some way or the other and humankind will have to learn to live with the changes."

Let me further summarize what Brother Rodney Brother is saying" said Malcolm, "and then we can move on to the next subject. Humankind can and should play a decisive role in dealing with the immensity and complexity of global warming. There are some obvious recognizable ways to deal with the situation and let me point out that the ways to deal with the situation does not only apply to the global warming. Earthlings should be respectful, considerate, and frugal in their daily ways of living. Being abusive, greedy, reckless and inconsiderate are values and principles that should govern our lives in all areas. That is before disasters, during and after."

"Let me reiterate and expand upon my fellow hosts words", interjected Sojourner. "We mentioned the problems of the homeless, world hunger, and wars. I say, grow food, feed the hungry; build homes, house the homeless. To many of you that may seem too simple, but food and shelter are basic human needs and the world has enough materials, produce, and manpower to provide these necessities for all. Now tell me what kind of sense because people can't pay their mortgages; People starving and begging for food and farmers plowing under crops and spilling milk to the land. And wars! Wars are criminal, sinful. Wars break *every one* of the Ten Commandments. Where is the godliness? Is there a sovereign relationship between Religion and Crime?"

This question produced exclamations and body shifting among the crowd. "What's that I hear, - Religion and Crime being mentioned as though they are partners?" Nanny the Maroon asked in all seriousness.

228

Kwame Ture answered her, "Whatever, - it boils down to a discussion on relationships between crime and religion. This is going to be one blazing discussion. Brother Malcolm should be a wizard at this coming from a life of crime to a very religious way of living."

"Don't short change Sojourner", chimed in June Jordan. "Both of those two are excellent candidates to discuss religion and crime. Sojourner's entire life was inspired by religion. From age five or six she was taught to look up to the heavens for God whenever she needed help. And we all know that when it comes to crime all who have experienced slavery are well aware of crimes being committed against them."

"I think the topic definitely requires some degree of clarification given the behavior of the earth folks. Sometimes you wonder about the speed in which religion becomes criminal and criminals gain religion. Michael Vick was as quick as his release of the ball on the football field when he repented his criminal behavior and found God", commented David Thoreau.

"Why pick on Vick", blurted Essex Hemphill. "What about all those religious leaders who con poor folks out of their hard earned money on Sundays? I call *that* a 'religious crime' or its akin to white collar crime in the way those offenders get away with it."

This stirring among the guest resulted in three loud taps resonating throughout the room. A hushed audience gave full attention as Sojourner began, "Neighbors, I know just about all of you are well acquainted with the sins of our fathers and mothers and sisters and brothers as well as we are acquainted with the goodness and holiness of those same kin. Too many folks think of religion as good and crime as bad. I ask you, how much space is there between good and bad? Is there good crime? Robin Hood and his followers thought so. These God Warriors that we saw in the much-publicized documentary, did their religion drive them to commit crimes? Brother Malik el Shabazz, speak to the people about Crime and Religion."

The centrality of personal expressiveness and the ethic of personal accountability were two of Malcolm's greatest strengths. His spontaneous expression of feelings and how he 'practiced what he preached', were endearing qualities. This evening he was in true form.

"I've lived a life of crime and I've lived a religious life and (*with a smile*) of course I still do. I used to believe that I was a criminal and jail terms were the consequences. You know how they make us believe that we reap what we sow, but I ask you, if you are given inferior, rotten, degenerative seeds to plant in contaminated, polluted soil, what can you reap but the products of the inferior materials? I have long since come to the position wherein I see acts labeled as crimes as a manipulative tool of governments. The establishment of laws governing certain behaviors and criminalizing those who break those laws enables the law makers to maintain codes of behavior beneficial to their personal and financial good." Malcolm paused to test the digestion rate of the folks.

Knowing Malcolm's propensity for speeches pregnant with new insights the audience was allowed to ask for clarification or inject questions at appropriate times. Little Esther without hesitation remarked, "Now I want to fully understand this. Are you implying that the law that says you ain't supposed to steal another person's car or jewelry or whatever, that that law was made for the good of, -well, for the good of who? I would surely want someone punished for stealing my car."

"Sister, stealing has become so well organized that it is an institution in itself. There is a whole system of rewards such as moneymaking and prestige. Car stealing and hi-jacking involves persons who can re-do the car so it can't be traced. Cars can be taken apart in minutes and parts sold. Stolen jewelry and pawnshops go hand in hand. Organized crime by definition I would say, involves pay back and pay back that goes way up the ladder involving top officials. Too often success is the results of organized protected crime, not hard honest labor.

230

But, back to the second part of your question about punishment. Who steals cars and why? The majority of stolen cars are part of an organized ring, a money making ring. America instills in people the need for conspicuous consumption, -have that new car, a Black in a Cadillac, man what more could you want, *(laughter)* fancy clothes and expensive jewelry, jewelry that you keep in a drawer more than 9/10 of its life, and how about that second home, one on Martha's Vineyard or in the Hamptons, a well paying professional job couldn't afford two homes, so do a little white collar crime on the side and get that second home that stays vacant most of the year.

There should be no need to steal a car, excluding those kids who go for a joy ride but I put that in a different category. I'm not legitimizing stealing. I'm analyzing the circumstances in society that promotes stealing. The idea that you need more, and more and more is a driving force."

"I still think someone should have to pay for committing a crime." Big Mama Thornton responds, "They say let the punishment fit the crime. So who steals cars must like cars, so put them to work washing cars, on the assembly line for cars, repairing cars, - and not taking a job away from someone else, no, they got to work off their crime."

Here Malcolm stopped, searched the audience, and located Dr. DuBois. Malcolm beckoned to W.E.B. DuBois and said, Brother DuBois recall what you said in 1959 about the manipulation of race and class in the service of wealth."

Graciously DuBois rose, and as testimony to his genius he re-iterated, "Perhaps the most extraordinary characteristic of current America is the attempt to reduce life to buying and selling. Life is not love unless love is sex bought and sold. Life is not knowledge save knowledge of technique, of science for destruction. Life is not beauty except for beauty for sale. Life is not art unless its price is high and it is sold for profit. All life is production for profit. And what is profit but for buying and selling again?" Still revealing a bit of his haughtiness, DuBois nodded and bowed from his waist in appreciation of the audiences' spontaneous applauses.

"Thank you, sir, for succinctly crystallizing my concept. Now those words were initially spoken in 1959 and they are just as apt today." Again, Dubois looking sharp, as were all the guests in their finery, acknowledged Malcolm's, thanks by nodding resolutely.

"Little Esther, I hope that answers your questions. The point I am making is that we are ruled by a minority with wealth and power. Let me tell you what I think is a crime." At this time, Malcolm's voice increased in volume and speed. "It's a crime to have children living in poverty and saying, 'here kitty, kitty' when the kitty is a rat. It's a crime to have children going to bed hungry living in overcrowded roach and rat infested apartments; it's a crime when pimping and prostituting and peddling drugs are sure ways of having a steady income; police brutality is a crime. And who are the real criminals? Let's start with the landlords who profit from their business or they wouldn't be in it; the people in City Hall who allow the slum lords to operate; the officials and politicians in State Capitals and the officials and politicians and Congress, all the law makers and law enforcement crooks."

Geronimo stood up, armed raised, waiting for recognition. "Brothers and sisters do not forget the Native Americans living on the reservations. Over 50% of the parents are out of work; there is no public transportation. It is nearly impossible to find trained doctors and nurses to live on the reservations. There are pockets of poverty across the United States, but those numbers are multiplied on the reservations. And I ask the questions, who are the criminals, the Indians who get drunk and are jailed, the many who commit suicide? No, the real criminals are the officials with governmental power who create the problems and allow these conditions to exist. Those 30 white founders of the Constitution of the United States of America termed treaties to be "the supreme law of the land", equal to the Constitution itself. Yet, the founders-and all the white men who followed them into power—broke every one of the 372 treaties signed between the U.S. government and Indians nations.

232

The law makers violated the laws and should have been prosecuted."

As soon as Geronimo completed his final sentence Running Eagle spoke without recognition but with passion, "And don't omit the millions of people in Haiti starving while tons of food rotted in containers in the nation's ports due to government red tape. It's outrageous. Tons of beans, rice and other staples rotting and being devoured by vermin while families starve. The people are forced to eat 'dirt cookies', made out of dirt, yes, earth dirt, salt, and vegetable oil. Under these conditions if a father or mother steals rice or beans for their children, are they criminals?"

Sojourner regained the microphone and calmly said, "Seems to me like I recall that Christian Relief Services are most instrumental in helping the Indians on the reservations. And the nuns and missionary workers who help in areas around the world when there are environmental calamities- they don't work for profit or prestige. We need to get on with the intersection of religion and crime."

"I'll try to be brief in setting the stage for this discussion" Malcolm began pacing the stage and rubbing his chin. "Books and scholars on the subject of religion have you to believe that there are five major world religions namely Judaism, Christianity, Islam, Hinduism, and Buddhism and these five religions have a combined membership of 3 to 4 billion people and that is about 80% of the world's population. I habitually question these types of statistics because the poll takers frequently misunderstand the power of the unregistered." Knowing this statement would generate questioning, he Malcolm quickly added, "By that I mean, well, take Haiti for example, the saying goes that in terms of religion the Haitian population is 90% Christian and 95 % Voudon. What I am implying is that there are many crossovers in religions. We hear talk about true believers and to that I say, they truly believe in what they want to believe, -in some cases a belief of some sort is necessary for their daily survival and in other cases the followers truly believe in following selective dictates of their religion and in accordance with their interpretation.

In the case of the former, and I am referring to the masses of people, women in particular and many men as well, who feel that they need to liberate themselves from the power and effects of sins and evil. Religious leaders like Daddy Grace, Father Divine, and Fred Price set themselves up as person capable of bringing salvation. In return, the followers give, donate, tithe, pledge their finances to these leaders. They, the givers, remain at the same economic level and the receivers grow richer and richer. On a much larger and grandiose style the Catholic churches follow a similar pattern."

"Brother Malcolm, folks go to church for reasons, spiritual and emotional reasons, -they go to church to have their needs filled, spiritual and emotional needs. Those preachers and pastors and priests, fulfill some of those needs and those preachers, pastors and priests aren't the ones who created those needs."

"Sister Sojourner, thank you for adding that important perspective. However, in the case of God's Warriors these religious believers and followers of God, ingest, internalize, pray, flagellate, discriminate, avenge, kill, murder, chastise, ostracize, - commit all sorts of what could be called crimes in the name of following the dictates of their Gods."

Mother Jones gained recognition and responded in hard tones. "Let's set the record straight. Religion has been referred to as the opiate of the masses, and it is true to the extent that the poorest and the oppressed need to be drugged to face the everyday realities of their lives and on the other hand the opiate serves to allow the opium givers to continue on their paths of living the ostentatious lives of the super rich. This practice seems to have no beginning or ending. Religion's role as a savior and benefactor of the savings has been with mankind since time began. What religion's role is supposed to be and how it plays out at times is contradictory, practically an oxymoron. Recently the Archdiocese of Chicago had

234

to pay more than $12.6 million to settle lawsuits by 16 people who accused priests of sexual abuse. Those priests must have lost the holy spirit."

Booker T. Washington was eager to have his say and with a friendly competitive glance at Dr. DuBois, he began, "Religion must be projected in its seminal intent. In many of my writings, I have emphasized the need to prepare our students to become responsible leaders and that learning/education is founded on **religious** and **academic** training. We find it a hard thing to make a good Christian of a hungry man. They may "get happy" and "shout" in church, but in addition, they need some form of industry to enable them to put food on the table. That is to say, religion and its accompanying morality must be part and parcel of industrial and intellectual development. Those who use the pulpit as a means of scalping devotees are making a sacrilege of religion."

"In the world it is difficult to escape the influences and practices of religion in ones daily routines. There are many whom I refer to as 'eclectic believers', -those that do a bit of Buddhism one day, go with friend to a Baptist congregation on Sunday and during the remainder of the week boast about aspects of their Catholic upbringing that they just can't shake. The growing numbers of mega-churches appeal to and attract hundreds of these 'eclectics'. For example, Rick Warren founding pastor of one of the country's largest churches with a 23,000 membership is bringing a new wardrobe to the Evangelical community. Pastor Warren is considered by many to be the most influential religious figure on the American political scene. He has a comprehensive biblical vision for world mission that moves beyond social conservatism to causes such as battling poverty, combating global warming, and a drive toward extending Sunday's spirituality to the rest of one's life. So here you have a megastar religious giant with connections to the White House, with an agenda to turn every single Christian church into a provider of local health care, economic development, literacy, and spiritual growth. However, his ideologies concerning homosexuality and abortion are obsolete and archaic. A powerful religious figure should not be oppressive to human diversity", said David Thoreau.

Sojourner recognized Emily Dickinson who had been politely asking for speaking time.

"I'm familiar with the personality and vitality of Pastor Warren as I am familiar with the stardom of Billy Graham. But, I want to hear what is being done about the deep-rooted sexism in the churches. The Vatican very recently rejected attempts by women to become priests in the Roman Catholic Church. And the Vatican had the unmitigated gall to reiterate a decree that anyone involved in ordination ceremonies is automatically excommunicated. Personally, I think the Catholic Church is grossly out of step with humanity. The Pope refuses to change traditional church teachings in divorce, abortion, euthanasia, gay marriages and the requirement that priests be male and celibate. I won't go so far as to say that such rulings contribute to the financial drain on funds due to paying millions in lawsuits for sexual abuse cases, but it is food for thought."

Amy Jacques eager to have her say exclaimed, "Religion and crime are two separate entities and never were designed to be inter-related, rather, one role of religion was to prevent crime teach people to live a moral, ethical life and to allow people to repent if they committed a crime. But unfortunately, individual and institutional malfeasance has resulted in religion being criminal and crimes being committed under religious headings.

Emily as a women's rights advocate you know I am for women having equal rights in religion as well as politics, however, there has to be struggle, protracted struggle, to bring about the changes and the Catholic Church will hold on to their argument that they are not authorized to change the will of Christ in the same manner that the anti-abolitionists held on to the belief that Blacks should remain slaves and have no right to vote.

236

On another note, just listen to this, in the USA it is reported that every 15 minutes a crime is committed. Yes, every 15 minutes and that's only the reported crimes. Crimes committed in the name of the Lord, crimes committed in the name of justice, crimes committed in the name of lust, crimes committed in the name of basic needs, and crimes committed in spite of God and religion."

Sister Sojourner took possession of the stage. "In the mid 1840's as history well knows, at a meeting in Faneuil Hall in Boston, after Frederick Douglas said that he had lost faith that Black Americans would ever gain justice from white Americans, I raised my voice and asked, *'Frederick, is God dead?'* "
A hush covered the ballroom. Without raising her voice, she spoke from the depth of her belief in God and even the crickets in the crevices of the amphitheater walls heard her. "I must ask again, 'Is God dead?' And the answer remains, only if you have lost touch with your belief in the spiritual ancestral God and allow some preaching man or woman to con you and rob you of your godly nature as well as your money. For those of you who believe in many Gods and those of you who do not believe in any God, may my God bless you, and keep you on the path of righteousness so that you will forever be able to know *when and why* you are committing a crime."

The Ancient Ancestors had been immobile in rapt attention to the entire discussion. As Sojourner completed her words there was a discernable bodily relaxation among the royal five as they wordlessly expressed their complacency.

Malcolm allowed time for the energies to relocate their selves then spoke, "And might I add that up here in the firmament, any formal religion that I might have followed while on earth is obsolete. By that, I mean, up here, we live a life of harmony and have full respect for one another, we harbor no ill will and we care and have compassion for one another, -so why would there be a need for the role of religion?"

There were no additional comments from the audience. Malcolm and Sojourner conferred and announced that there would be a 20-minute break before starting the subjects, racism and education.

Twenty minutes later three taps from the walking stick and the final formal aspect of the conference began. The hosts stood together at the podium both looking as if they had just emerged from the fountains of energy and vitality. Neither one sat during the entire evening's program.

Sojourner began, "We welcome you back from your mini-break and pleased that none were dilatory."

Then Malcolm, "Now that you are re-vitalized and, by the way, we arranged for this topic to be presented after the break for just that reason, the topics of Racism and Education are always a high energy affair.

Let me begin by saying that I find it boring rather than enlightening to hear the same dismal statistics and facts about racism and education when it comes to Blacks and other non-white populations. Year after year, we hear that Black students have the highest dropout rates. The only changes are the names of the students. Their illiteracy stage seems to stop progressing after the 3rd grade.

Black infant death rate is highest in the nation with Black infant mortality rate being 13.6% compared to the nation's overall rate of 6.86; When it comes to AIDS, Blacks represent one in eight Americans, yet they account for one in every two people living with AIDS. As for the homeless, there are more homeless people in this country today than any time since the Great Depression.

And the prison population, for the first time in U.S. history, more than one of every 100 adults is in jail or prison, according to a new report documenting America's rank as the world's number 1 incarcerator. While one in 30 men between the ages of 20 and 34 is behind bars, for Black males in that age group it is one in nine. For

238

women, one in every 355 white women aged 35 to 39 is behind bars, for Black women it is one in every 100 in that same age group." Malcolm shook his head ruefully as he spoke, "Those stats are disgusting, repetitive, a criminal shame."

Pausing a moment he launched into his recitation. "In the summer of '67, ghettos in cities across white America exploded as African Americans rebelled yet again against the tyrannies of poverty, police brutality, and white injustice. A presidential National Advisory Council on Civil Disorders, Kerner Commission, was established to find out what happened, why it happened, and what could be done to prevent it from happening again. The 1968 Kerner Commission reported, "What white Americans have never fully understood—but what the Negro can never forget—is that white society is deeply implicated in the ghetto. White institutions created it, white institutions maintain it, and white society condones it." The Commission concluded that to prevent such "civil disorders" in the future, the country would have to commit billions and billions of dollars to eradicate poverty and reconstruct central cities ghettos and barrios devastated by decades and decades of white institutional racism.

Now that was almost 40 years ago and what do we have? A continuation of ghetto up-risings and an increase in crime, same old poverty rates, school drop outs still dropping out with regularity, police brutalities continue but now they are being videoed by bystanders and homeless population a national tragedy."

The format for the evening encouraged dialogue so Malcolm engaged the people. "Do you see the connection or a relationship between these statistics and racism and education?"

Mabel Hampton sitting next to Bob Moore nudged him to speak out. She was familiar with the exceptional work he had done on racism, multiculturalism, anti-racism, and education. Seeing that he was hesitant to speak up she warned him that if he didn't she would introduce him as that good looking white boy with the curly black hair and razor sharp mind who is a re-incarnated Black scholar. Knowing that she would, reluctantly he stood up.

"Ah, young Dr. Robert Moore, let us hear your profound assessment on this subject or should I say subjects. What's new and different in the world of education and racism?"

With his hands in his back pockets and shifting from one foot to the other, his opening sentence reflected his years of involvement and research on the subjects. "In 1984 I gave a talk titled, *"School Systems Perpetuate Racism, and Don't Know It: Can We Deal with It?"* I will talk from the contents of that paper. I once heard Paulo Freire, the great Brazilian educator—indeed world educator—speak and he noted that in the Third World illiteracy is a product of the lack of schools while in a society like the United States, illiteracy is a product of the schools. If we want to understand racism in our societies and in our schools, we need to focus on the organized practices and policies that perpetuate racism. Unfortunately, educational institutions are among the leading institutions wherein racism flourishes."

"Give us some examples before you sit down. We're not finished hearing from you"

"For decades there has been exploration of the nature of racism in education though actual change has been negligible. We know how racist practices and policies such as tracking, unequal funding, staffing patterns, IQ testing, culturally biased testing, lack of community control, lack of effective bi-lingual/bicultural programming, lack of sensitivity to diverse learning styles contribute to the unequal outcome of schooling in our society."

"Brother Bob", Essex Hemphill raised his voice, "I was so tired of hearing educated, bright, Earthfolks mis-use the word racism and with authority. Would you please give us a definitive definition?"

"O.K. Essex, here it is but I will tie it in with the word multiculturalism as a social, emotional, and political goal we seek

240

to attain in societies composed of people of many racial backgrounds and cultural traditions. The goal of a truly humane, democratic, just society for all women and men is a society not divided by race, culture, ethnicity, religion, sexual preference, age physical disability or any other reason people suffer discrimination."

"That's like it is up here. A true Utopia," muttered Babe Zaharias.

"Althea Gibson nudged her saying, "Shush, let's hear this definition of racism."

"A major obstacle to the realization of multiculturalism is racism," Bob continued. "By 'racism' I do not mean attitudes that one racial group may hold about their own or another racial group. Such attitudes are 'prejudices'- racial prejudice being the pre-judgment of others based on race. Racism includes racial prejudices but it is much more. Racism involves **power**. The power exercised by one racial group to impose its prejudices, its interests, and its will on other racial groups. It is systematic oppression of one race over another."

"That's a mouth full, Bob, a good solid mouthful to digest, but it is important to add that 'race' and 'racial groups' are concepts created by European men to justify their domination of non-European people. Race has no scientific validity as a way of dividing humankind. But it has real social validity in deciding the way which humankind has been divided."

"I hear you loud and clear Mr. Carter G. Woodson, but you and Bob seem to be beating up on European men as if we were all one monolithic personality. There are many of us who have fought the battle against racism for a life time," said Eugene Debs as John Brown and William Lloyd Garrison provided the Amen Corner."
Rosa Luxemburg convincingly added, "Don't leave this European woman out. I as a European woman fought my share of battles."

"Carter G. I agree with Brother Eugene and Sister Rosa and that's what's so good about these meetings. When one person is short sighted, another will contribute with a broader perspective."

The audience was well into the debates, their bodies in tune with thoughts, and showing an eagerness to be expressed. When a subject or topic got rolling those present could stand and make remarks to the speaker without recognition from the chair.

Frederick Douglas: "Recall, my heavenly friends, my slave master's remark about me, 'Education would unfit him to be a slave.' This could explain why so many schools function so effectively to produce such illiteracy among Black and Latino students. A good education would "unfit" them to be employed in skilled jobs."

Gwendolyn Brooks: "Language develops out of culture. Just look at dictionary definitions for 'white' and 'black', the English language reflects the ways in which English-speaking cultures influence racial attitudes about Black and White people. White and Black--Good and Bad."

Geronimo: "The word 'massacre' is used when Indians win, while 'victory' is when whites win."

Minnie Hollow Wood: "Racial imagery pervades U.S. culture as it shapes images of people. The 'Indian Princess' on the Land-O-Lakes butter boxes has such European features that the only clue that she is an 'Indian' is a feather stuck in her head and that garb wrapped around her."

James Baldwin: "Racism with all its venomous appendages must be fought, but fighting racism is like fighting oatmeal."

Sylvia Plath: "Facing and dealing with racism is an exceptionally difficult process for those of us who are white, but there must be daily challenges. As white, lesbian, Jewish poet Adrienne Rich has

242

observed, "an unexamined white perspective leads to dangerous ignorance, heart-numbing indifference, and complacency."

Zora Neale Hurston: "Why do students in the classrooms learn to celebrate Patrick Henry crying, "Give me liberty or give me death", while holding African people enslaved and denying all women the liberties he sought for himself, while they don't celebrate Abigail Adams who spoke out against slavery and the rights for women? Why, because of a racist education system."

Kwame Nkrumah: "As the first elected president of an independent Ghana- let me say this much- one new head can not change a country that is overburdened with oppressive, racist, economic and political baggage. Parliaments, assemblies, congresses and above all masses of people must insist on and fight for the needed changes."

Malcolm was boyishly animated as he glanced on Sojourner's direction and noticed the energy surrounding her was shifting into high gear, then neutral, as she and her Lumumba walking stick took center stage. 'Folks, it's Sojourner time', he mused.

She looked out over her audience with admiration, satisfaction, and love. These were all her heavenly people and despite their acknowledgement of the Earthfolks confusion, problems and wrong doings, respect, compassion and concern for them existed and a desire for their success and happiness in the very difficult world they established.

"My friends in the firmament, chilluns were not born with racist attitudes and behaviors and usually they don't choose to be that way. The racist problems in the schools do not reflect the natural state of human interactions. No, the racist behaviors are the symptoms of social conditions in institutions like schools, and they, the institutions, keep racism alive. White chilluns are not born racist and Black chilluns are not born unfit. To the extent that they are, Earthfolks make them that way and the power is in their hands to make it not so. We up here, high above the pollution hope and pray for their betterment."

Malcolm moved to stand by his compatriot and together they offered a blessing giving thanks for the success of the evening. The festivities that followed included refreshments that showed off the special foods of the communities. Music was provided by the big swing bands and later jazz. Dances from every conceivable era - the quadrille, minuet, cake walk, waltz, two-step, Mandy Strut, lindy hop, Lambert Walk, buck and wing, - was a sight that was inconceivable unless viewed personally. Later when the specially prepared chilled grape juices were served, operatic arias were listened heard.

The Ancient Ancestors enjoyed the music, imbibed in their specially prepared beverages, paid homage to their hosts, and as royally as they arrived, departed gently and swiftly in the cloud mobile.

The Retreat members satiated themselves with music, dance food and beverages, talked, cajoled and enjoyed one another to their individual satiation points.

The awesome fascination of the clouds, as dawn approached, once again held the attention of Sojourner and Malcolm as they sat side by side in rocking chairs, bidding adieu to each departing member. The sunrays spread over miles of skies and cloud formations, coloring them magnificent hues. Sojourner's dark, perspicacious, wisdom filled eyes, met Malcolm's lighter colored, perspicacious, insightful eyes. Wordlessly but with feelings so intense that the birds, bees, butterflies and those crickets in the walls, felt the warmth, and harmony between them and the satisfaction of knowing that their world was in perfect order. Simultaneously the two Retreat favorites rose and began their stroll down the Glory Road Boulevard to their respective domains.

The End

Chapter Eleven Glossary and Endnotes

- *Ella Fitzgerald (1918-1996):* Known as the *"First Lady of Song"* Ella Fitzgerald was born in Newport News, Virginia and raised in an orphanage in Yonkers, New York. Her road to stardom is credited to Chick Webb a famous jazz drummer and bandleader. In 1938, Ella composed her most famous song, *"A Tisket A Tasket"* based on an old nursery rhyme and became an immediate success. She had the ability to sing swing, ballad, pop, calypso, Dixieland jazz, but is best known for her "scat" singing, a style and form she practically invented. Ella recorded more than 2000 songs and had more than 70 albums to her credit. She influenced several generations of singers.

- *Burning suit:* In the book, <u>*Malcolm X: The End of World Supremacy-Four Speeches,*</u> in the Introduction by Benjamin Goodman he refers to a particular clothing that Malcolm wore when he was fully prepared and intended to give a very deep lecture. He would wear a blue suit and red tie. This was referred to as his "burning suit."

- *Millerites*: Father William Miller was one of a legion of dispensationalists who made calculations about the end of time based on the numbers cited in the Book of Daniel. In 1843, the year of Sojourner's rebirth, she spent time among different groups of Millerite strongholds.

- *Racial Prejudices and Racism:* The material and definitions of racism, prejudices and multiculturalism were taken from the following as yet unpublished speeches and essays of Robert Moore:

  > *1. The Cultural Perpetuation of the Rightness of Whiteness*
  > *2. Workshop/Seminar Multiculturalism Racism and the School System*
  > *3. Native American Information Packet; A Review*
  > *4. 200 Years of White Racism: No Cause for Celebration Equity in an Era of Diversity Conference School District of Philadelphia 1987*

- *Sisyphus:* A legendary king of Corinth condemned eternally to repeat the cycle of rolling a heavy rock up a hill in Hades only to have it roll down again as it nears the top continuously. *"You never get where you're going."*

Essay #1: Sojourner Truth: Archetypal Black Feminist

By Gloria I. Joseph, Ph D
From *Wild Women in the Whirlwind: Afra American Culture and the Contemporary Literary Renaissance* © 1990

Who was this woman called Sojourner Truth? Isabella Baumfree was her given name, her surname being a Dutch nickname applied to her father. It is said that Sojourner Truth was born in 1797 but her birth was not accurately recorded. The vital statistics of Black people were customarily left unrecorded because of then-prevailing attitudes: "Negras aren't thoroughbreds and one doesn't make a fuss over registering a litter of mutts." It is known that Sojourner was born in the latter part of the eighteenth century in New York State's Ulster County; she died November 26, 1883, and was buried in Oak Hill Cemetery in Battle Creek, Michigan.

Sojourner Truth has been described as an abolitionist, lecturer, women's rights activist, freedom fighter, domestic servant, evangelist, author, social worker, and a concerned and militant champion for the rights of her Black brothers and sisters. To list these occupations and roles, however, does not do justice to Sojourner's superordinate experiences, her uncanny wit, or her intellectual genius. As an archetypal Black feminist, Sojourner was a revolutionary whose life reflected the integrity and commitment to oppose any force that sought to deny Black people and other oppressed groups their basic human rights and dignity. Fighting personal and institutional bias during the period in which she lived, she charted a new way of existing on the shores of North America.

Sojourner was a prototype of generations of Black women to follow who would possess a strong sense of self as a Black person and a female. Her antiracist and anti-sexist consciousness opposed the oppression and the exploitation of the many for the few. During the antebellum history of the United States, she emerged as a precursor of Black women activists involved in the struggle to

247

overcome racism, classism, and heterosexism, as well as sexism in the New World. In her life span, she used her experiences and those of other Black women as a barometer for articulating and taking measures for social· change, and as a gauge for assessing the viability of proposed social tactics or policy reforms. Many Black women, also of the belief that gender and patriarchy were as central as race and class to understanding historical phenomena, would in her wake express her revolutionary ideas and emulate her deeds.

On the basis of her deeds and accomplishments, her name should be as well known as Susan B. Anthony, Elizabeth Cady Stanton, and Jane Addams. Among famous Black personages in history, her name should be side by side with W E. B. DuBois, Frederick Douglass, and Harriet Tubman. Her witticisms and adages are equal to those of Will Rogers and Benjamin Franklin, and her acts of courage comparable to those of Joan of Arc and Marie Curie. Instead, she remains one of the Black women whose histories have not adequately been treated. When her name is recognized in academic arenas, it is most often associated with her "Ain't I a Woman" speech, her peculiar grammar, and her heroic acts. Rarely is there any mention of the philosophical constructs and revolutionary concepts underlying her words and deeds.

A frightening example of the way in which Sojourner is known was made clear to me in one of my classes while teaching at Cornell University in the activist Sixties. I asked the class, which to my pleasure had a large number of Black students, "Who was Sojourner Truth?" A female student, with a look of pride and some arrogance, boldly explained to the class that "Sojourner Truth was a Black woman who white people thought was a man, and at a conference when a white man teased her calling her a man, she opened her dress and exposed her breasts to prove she was a woman." I was utterly astonished and kept my amazement under control as I explained that Sojourner's greatness did not lie in the fact that she was not a transvestite!

Nearly twenty years since that incident, too little of substance has been written about the profoundness and progressive-mindedness of this incredible woman. The experiences of Sojourner Truth have been recorded with a superwoman motif: a Black oddity with mysterious powers and great physical strength. Few historians have described her as a person of great mental and spiritual depth; a woman who earned worldwide fame for her stance on slavery, temperance, penal reform, and women's rights. There is a twenty-two-cent commemorative stamp honoring her in the Black Heritage Series; several women's organizations and publications are named after her; and about a half dozen authors have written books about her. Although honored in this way, why is the recognition so paltry given the magnitude of her greatness?

The current Women's Movement has brought Sojourner to the attention of feminists, but she is usually included as an "also ran" while the greatness and exploits of the pre- and post-Civil War white feminists and abolitionists are often extolled. Many of her feats remain unheralded. For example, relatively well known is the heroic behavior of Rosa Parks, a Black seamstress who-when she refused to give up her seat to a white man on a segregated bus in Montgomery, Alabama-sparked the Civil Rights Movement in 1955 with Black people's successful bus boycott. Virtually unknown is the fact that Sojourner was responsible for integrating a local transportation system. In the early 1860s, Sojourner protested Black people's restriction to Jim Crow cars. Her complaints led to congressional action banning segregated cars in the District of Columbia.

Passing the law itself did not mean that it would be followed, so Sojourner battled repeatedly with conductors who did not want to enforce the law. She confronted and combated streetcar drivers and conductors and infuriated passengers, but she persevered. When drivers ignored her signal that indicated she wanted to board, she would cry out in her inimitable voice, "I WANT TO RIDE!"

And ride she did. On one occasion, she encountered a conductor who tried to shove her from the streetcar. In the fracas, Sojourner suffered a dislocated shoulder. She took her case to court, won, and the conductor lost his job. Sojourner's comment after the tremendous victory was, "Before the trial was ended, the inside of the cars looked like pepper and salt." (1) This was one of many performances that attest to the vigilance with which Sojourner adhered to her principles, her courage in confronting injustice, and her wisdom in selecting appropriate actions. Almost a century apart, Rosa Parks and Sojourner Truth fought similar battles-battles they waged on behalf of themselves and, simultaneously, in the interests of the larger Black community.

Perhaps the relative dearth of critical studies about Sojourner Truth can be attributed to the claim that she was not a literate woman. Sojourner did not leave behind numerous treatises and books, or reams of scholarly writings and oratory. Yet, as Angela Davis noted of Harriet Tubman in 1971, Sojourner Truth's place in the Western intellectual tradition is not commensurate with her role and "has been consistently and grossly minimized."(2) Surely, Sojourner's legacy was as much her revolutionary philosophy as her activism—as an unflinching advocate of the human rights of the oppressed, especially Black people and all women.

There are, in the last decade, some writings that have begun to contextualize Sojourner in proper historical perspective as both an activist *and* a theorist in the *Black* and Women's liberation struggles of her day. They include Beverly Guy-Sheftall's "Remembering Sojourner Truth: On Black Feminism," *Catalyst;* Bettina Aptheker's *Women's Legacy: Essays* on *Race, Sex, and Class;* Victoria Ortiz's *Sojourner Truth: A Self-Made Woman,* a well-researched young adult book; and Raya Dunayevskaya's considerable works which consistently acknowledge Sojourner as a woman of both "revolutionary force" and "revolutionary reason."

Historical accounts of Sojourner's life commonly cite that Sojourner was deeply religious and that her beliefs had a great bearing on the way in which she lived her life. Her piety is invariably placed within the context of Western, patriarchal, organized religion and not within the African culture with which she and many other of her contemporary Black brethren were closely identified. But if Sojourner's religious experience was in any way typical of the millions of African people in the Americas, it can be reasonably assumed that her beliefs were informed by a combination of the African world-view and the Judeo-Christian ethic. (3)

To examine the life of Sojourner within· the framework of African cosmology and epistemology provides a deeper understanding of her activism, her thinking, and· the legacy she left for Black feminists. In addition to her life setting forth the parameters of activism exercised by Black women today, her radical ideas remain a part of Black people's collective consciousness. Her words and deeds were wholly consistent with an Afro-centric perspective that African-American women activists assert in these times, distinguishing themselves as *Black* feminists.

The African world-view provides insight into the manner in which Sojourner lived her life-a style that has been interpreted as fearless, peculiar, extraordinary, and unique. African cosmology grows out of a fundamental belief in an indivisible and inexhaustible relationship among God, mankind, and the cosmos. (4) From the Afro-centric perspective, the material and spiritual world are inseparable-a view which informed all aspects of the social, political, educational, moral, and psychological dimensions of African community life. The quality of "fearlessness" associated with Sojourner could very well have been based upon her unequivocal dedication to structuring her reality to maximize the possibility of the most positive, earthly experience. Since (the African) reality is at once both spiritual and material, all is interrelated, interdependent, interconnected, and integrated. In this way of looking at things, everything becomes "spirit manifest." There is no "pie in the sky" separate from a hellish material existence.

Characterization of Sojourner as "extraordinary," "peculiar," and "unique" might also be traceable to her African world-view. In many traditional African societies, women were socially and economically independent and held in high esteem; aspects of egalitarian social organization were carried to and retained in the Americas by African people. Debunking the Western claim that women's autonomy was "foreign to the cultural heritages of Third World peoples," Eleanor Leacock wrote in the 1980s that, even today, ~'women anthropologists ... are finding many attitudes and practices that indicate women's former status and persisting importance. (5) Undoubtedly, the prejudices of the times in which Sojourner lived did not validate her on any level-as a Black person, woman, slave, or domestic servant. To speak or act independently in the face of such prevalent biases would have provoked a range of reactions. Thus, for Sojourner, validation of her sense of mission and her importance as an African woman would have found only one source-the African world-view.

The oneness of reality and the principle of women's autonomy inherent in the Afro-centric world-view were constantly demonstrable in Sojourner's words and deeds. This is why she expressed incredulity and impatience when she confronted the passivity of feminists in the Women's Movement. Basically in agreement with the women's rights activists of her time, among them Lucy Stone, Lucretia Mott, Frances Gage as well as Susan B. Anthony and Elizabeth Cady Stanton, Sojourner Truth had a different outlook concerning direct action. For example, in 1850 at a women's conference, Sojourner had pointedly informed her counterparts, "Sisters, I aren't clear what you be after. If women want any rights more than they got, why don't they just take them and not be talking about it?" (6) Without fear of ostracism, Sojourner's passionate commitment to the need and urgency for social action reflected a blanket assumption that militancy was right. After all, by the logic of the Afro-centric perspective, the spirit is manifest in what one does and does not do.

The uncompromising stand Sojourner took in the face of the proposed Fourteenth Amendment to the United States Constitution vividly exemplifies her fearlessness, her staunch devotion to a qualitative experience in the "here and now." The Amendment that gave Black males the vote but omitted any reference to women, outraged white suffragettes who felt betrayed. Previously

252

in 1848 at the historic Seneca Falls Convention, Frederick Douglass had delivered an eloquent plea on behalf of women's right to vote. But by 1867, after the Civil War, it was Sojourner who stood alone for the all-but-forgotten Black women. Frederick Douglass and Frances Watkins, both Black activists, and Wendall Phillips and Abby Keely Foster, white longtime supporters of the Women's Movement, uniformly argued that the Black male slave's suffering entitled him to prior consideration.

The political perspicacity of Sojourner was obvious as she spoke to the issue of enfranchisement in her deep, sonorous voice: "My friends, I come from another field-the country of the slave. They have got the liberty—so much good luck to have slavery partly destroyed, not entirely. I want it root and branch destroyed. Then we will all be free indeed~ I have a right as much as a man." She continued, "There is a great deal of stir about colored men getting their rights but not a word about the colored women's theirs, you see, the colored man will be masters over the women, and it will be 'just as bad as it was before. So I am for keeping the thing going while things are stirring, because if we wait 'till it is still, it will take a great while to get it going again." (7)

Sojourner was doggedly vigilant in not accepting anything short of full recognition of Black women's equality. Importantly, her reasoning is the genesis of parallel activity among twentieth-century Black feminists who have extended the Civil Rights and Black Power struggles of the fifties and sixties into an African-American feminist movement, "keeping the thing going while things are stirring."

Sojourner's words over a century ago imparted a consciousness of what contemporary African-American feminists have termed "the simultaneity of oppression." Speaking as a Black person and a woman, Sojourner identified patriarchal domination as another form of oppression. In her essay, "The Black Dimension in Women's Revolution," Raya Dunayevskaya aptly poses the question, "Have we even today, as we inveigh against 'male domination,' compared that to Sojourner's separation from

Frederick Douglass after the Civil War for being 'short-minded' because he did not wish to burden the struggle for the passage of the Fourteenth Amendment by demanding also the right of women to vote?" (8) Sojourner Truth's concept of "short minded" was a new language of thought for those who would impose a limitation to freedom.

Like David Walker's *Appeal to the Colored Citizens of the World* in 1829, Sojourner's appeal was pregnant with recognition that the suffering of any group or individual was wrong. Sojourner stood, in effect, fiercely committed to the logic of the Afro-centric world-view: any form of bondage is antithetical to God; a spiritual essence, consciousness, or energy that underlies the totality of creation. Suffering by God's creations assails God.

Although some might argue that Sojourner's views were typical of the feminist consciousness of her associates, it merits mention that Sojourner did not identify with the feminists of her period, only their common political objectives. Her ridicule of their class frivolity often provoked criticism from those who thought her behavior inappropriate for a woman. Imagine the nineteenth-century women's rights activists seated in the audience as Sojourner demanded, "What kind of reformers are you, with goose-wings on your heads, as if you were going to fly, and dressed in such ridiculous fashion, talking about reform and women's rights. It appears to me, you had better reform yourselves first." (9)

Another essential component of Afro-centric thought is sacrifice. (10) It is not conceived of as giving up or relinquishing something, as in the Western concept, but rather as a redistribution of necessary energy-a redistribution of the life force that permeates all living things and that is the power behind all living things.

In the African world-view, an unwillingness or failure to redistribute energy for the betterment of the world is no more than ungodly and requires active "reform." Sojourner's forceful honesty caused many of her white feminist associates to react with feigned and true horror. A present-day parallel is that of white feminists who are intimidated when Black feminists challenge stinginess or preoccupation with academic chatter and glamour in the face of the blight of apartheid and other human catastrophes.

The problems she faced as a Black woman in the 1800's are similar to ones Black women face today. Now as in yesteryear, an inordinate number of Black women live in poverty and raise children single-handedly, on scandalously pitiful incomes, while corporate America's living standards are shamefully opulent. Her observations of the condition of the poor in New York during the mid-1840s sound as if she were assessing the society in 1989: "Truly, here the rich rob the poor and the poor rob each other." (11)

Sojourner's work with the freed slaves after the Civil War provided her with the opportunity to understand more fully how the lives of her people were used for the enrichment of others. She detailed with painstaking accuracy how the vast and manifold contributions that Black people had made to the development of the United States had yet to be acknowledged or rewarded. "We have been a source of wealth to this republic," she proclaimed. "Our nerves and sinews, our tears and blood, have been sacrifices on the altar of this nation's avarice. Our unpaid labor has been a stepping-stone to its financial success. Some of its dividends must surely be ours." (12) How often is Sojourner Truth's name associated with this revolutionary concept of reparations, a theme which has been extolled by numerous Black Power advocates?

From the Afro-centric perspective, Sojourner's work among those who lived in misery and poverty in Freedman's Village in Virginia should not be equated with sacrifice of her life to work among the "wretched of the earth." The underlying aim of the Afro-centric conceptual system is to achieve everlasting peace and happiness. Her work, therefore, represented an attempt to achieve a perpetual state of bliss for humankind through a redistribution of energy to create a life force. In terms of the African cosmology, what happens to one affects all. Modern expressions of this type of thinking were Black women's activism and credo which focused upon stemming the mysterious murders of Black children in Atlanta, Georgia: "Atlanta is all of us."

Sojourner's involvement with diverse groups in a variety of settings and often under trying conditions conformed to the African world-view. Interpersonal relationships are accorded highest value in the Afro-centric conceptual system in contrast to the Western belief system in which the highest value of existence is the acquisition of material objects. Sojourner's cooperation with even hostile elements was fraught with a mindfulness of her intrinsic - value and what constituted Godliness. "Take ... how she handled the hypocritical ministers [white Abolitionists] who were taunting her, when she asked, 'Don't you believe in Jesus?' And when they said they did, how she told them, 'Well, Jesus is the son of God and Mary. Man had nothing to do with it.'" (13)

From the Afro-centric perspective, Sojourner's remarks were more than statements of Christian religious fact. If there is an "indivisible and inexhaustible relationship among God, mankind and the cosmos," then the clergy's blatant contempt for her divorced them from any affinity to Jesus. By the African world-view, all creations are valued manifestations of God. This world-view and her place within it gave her full license to respond without trepidation.

"I can't read, but I can read people," a characteristic Sojourner quote, could very well have been the postscript for her encounter with the Christian clergy. It would have been an appropriate statement in light of African epistemology. According to Linda Myers, "In the Afro-centric vein we assume self-knowledge is the basis of all knowledge, and one knows through symbolic imagery and rhythm. To the extent that we have assumed that self-knowledge is the basis of all knowledge and we are knowing more and more about this one essential essence, then how this essence is manifesting, how it's appearing, becomes extraordinarily critical." (14) Placing Sojourner within her African heritage, the declaration that she could "read people" represented an expressed confidence

256

in her ability to identify the spiritual essence of others based upon her knowledge of self.

Sojourner is tied to Black feminists of today not only by a condition, but also by a collective consciousness based on a way of knowing that is distinctly African. Explaining the process of knowing that underlies African cosmology, Myers states:

> "Everything in experience becomes a symbol or symbolic of infinite spirit-symbolic imagery. Whatever is coming into experience, into five-sense awareness, is automatically processed. It is processed not just by the count-and-measure-data, but also by the extrasensory acknowledgement that this is indeed spirit manifesting. In addition to knowing through this symbolic imagery, we also have to add rhythm. This is extra-ordinarily critical because everything that comes into experience is not "real." It is necessary to make a determination based upon the rhythm, based upon the nature of the inter-relatedness, the relationship of this appearing to what we already know is true." (15)

Sojourner's power as an African-American woman hinged on her extrasensory processing of "infinite spirit-symbolic imagery" using rhythm and judging the imagery's interrelatedness to determine the truth of the imagery. Grounded in African epistemology and cosmology, this is the same power Black feminists are reasserting by reclaiming their African roots. They repossess the strength of the personal within the realm of a world-view which links the spiritual dimension with the political dimension of their lives.

The bountiful accomplishments of Sojourner Truth deserve in depth analysis if for no other reason than their continuing social relevance. Immediately after the official abolition of slavery, Sojourner was on the frontlines for civil rights, women's rights, and Black Power, including the desegregation of public transportation, voting rights, and reparations-battles that have continued into the second half of the twentieth century.

Western ethnocentric intellectualism and cultural imperialism are prime reasons for scholars being blind to Sojourner's magnitude among history scholars, it has not been a popular tradition to conduct research on Black slave women. Western scholars have also dismissed her Black culture and her Black experiences. Certainly, too many academicians are content to ignore the retention of Africanisms by Black slaves and their descendants in the New World.

The late Raya Dunayevskaya has been one of a handful of white scholars to criticize the feminist historical analysis of the women's rights movement:

> All underestimate the Black dimension which inspired the white, middle-class, educated women to strike out on their own. Sojourner Truth· and sometimes also Harriet Tubman are dutifully mentioned, condescendingly, admitting their bravery- and of course their suffering as slaves-but never as Reason which drove the educated to face reality: that the Black women were the orators, generals, yes, thinkers. (16)

That Sojourner was not only brave but also an orator, general, and a *thinker* challenges all feminists, especially Black feminists, to see about the critical, historical contextualization of Sojourner Truth. Dunayevskaya appropriately has stated that "there is no such thing as women's history that is not the actual history of humanity's struggle toward freedom"; she simultaneously has called upon feminists to learn "the language of thought, Black thought." (17) Appreciation of an African-centered consciousness is essential to unearthing the contributions and legacy of Sojourner Truth.

Sojourner Truth must be seen in the contexts of an Afro-centric worldview and of her revolutionary intellect. Although in an alien land, she was heir to an African reality in which the material and spiritual worlds are one-spirit manifest. Her God was one of positive action, and she invoked this God in all of her

258

revolutionary activity. Consistent, despite criticisms, taunting, and attempts at subordination by members of the many communities with whom she worked, she would not compromise her principles. Her militant ideas were born of the scope of her life experiences, and self-knowledge was the core of her power. Sojourner is an archetypal personage, a forerunner and model for contemporary Black feminists as they struggle for freedom and justice in her image.

Notes

1   Victoria Ortiz, *Sojourner Truth: A Self-Made Woman* (New York: Lippincott Company, 1974), p. 81.

2   Angela Y. Davis, "Reflections on the Black Woman's Role in the Community of Slaves," *The Black Scholar* 3 (December 1971), 9.

3   See Robert Farris Thompson, *Flash of the Spirit* (New York: Vintage Books, 1984).

4   For a discussion of the literature, see Charlyn Harper, "How to Think Black: Toni Cade Bambara's *The Salt Eaters,"* Black Studies, No.6 (1983-1984),35.

5   Eleanor Burke Leacock, *Myths of Male Dominance: Collected Articles* on *Women Cross-Culturally* (New York: Monthly Review Press, 1981), pp.314-315.

6   Ortiz, *Sojourner Truth,* pp. 82-83.

7   Jeanne Deroin and Pauline Roland, *Sojourner Truth: Keeping the Thing Going While Things Are Stirring,* reprint from An American Women's Movement, pp. 129-130

8   Raya Dunayevskaya, "The Black Dimension in Women's Liberation," in *Women's Liberation and the Dialectics of Revolution* (Atlantic Highlands, N.J.. Humanities Press International. Inc., 1985), pp. 49-50.

9   Ortiz, *Sojourner Truth,* p. 138.

10   Harper, "How to Think Black," 38.

11   Ortiz, *Sojourner Truth,* p. 119.

12   Ibid. p. 121.

13   Dunayevskaya, "Black Dimension," p. 185.

14   For a full discussion of the literature, see Dr. Linda James Myers, "How to Think Black: Toni Cade Bambara's *The Salt Eaters,"* *Black Studies,* No.5 (1983-1984), 40.
15   Ibid., p. 41.
16   Dunayevskaya, "Black Dimension," p. 80.
17   Ibid.

Essay #2: Malcolm X Keynote Address—May 19th, 1987

First Symposium - Studies on Malcolm X
Sara Delano Roosevelt Memorial House—49 East 65th Street—
New York
Gloria I. Joseph, Ph.D.

The first time I saw and heard Malcolm was at Cornell University, Ithaca, New York, in the early 60's. In one speech he crystallized all the fragmented ideas and vacillating feelings about being Black in America, into a social and political construct that left no doubt as to who were the victims, who were the oppressors and that racism is an integral part of the root system of America's liberty tree. In that speech that evening his wit and genius inspired and energized me and gave me unconditional strength to be able to look white corporate America dead in the eye and respond to its shenanigans with a political analysis as to why there is oppression based on race, sex and class.

I was thoroughly fascinated with the spirited confidence with which he fielded questions from the audience. I went to the lecture with three other Blacks, and we were all filled with pride as we left the auditorium. In addition, I had a sense of growth that comes from newly acquired knowledge that has real meaning. Since that initial exposure to Malcolm, every future contact was an additional learning experience. For example, I distinctly remember him saying on one occasion, with regard to questions, "deal with the intent of the question, not just the well phrased words." This has helped me deal with many questions from white racists and feminists.

When I referred to the fact that Malcolm influenced my Afro-centric conceptual thought, and used the term "Thinking Black", that simple phrase is critical—it is the kernel—of Black liberation theory. Without this consciousness, an individual is like a fortress with no weaponry for battle. It looks the part, has the right label, but is relatively meaningless, and definitely harmless. Thinking

261

Black is not something new. It embodies African epistemology—that branch of philosophy that deals with the origin of knowledge, the methods and limits of knowledge—or more simply put—how we know what we know.

We have been given messages and information about how to think Black ever since there has been Black people. For example: W.E. B. Dubois told us that African-American people had to become wed with truth to dwell above the veil. He was talking about thinking Black; Johari Amini says that we have to develop a new concept of what is and what is not. That is thinking Black Lerone Bennett says that we have to develop a radical re-evaluation about our ideas of history. That is thinking Black. Molefi Asante has said that we have to look out from our OWN center, through our OWN Afro-centric eyes. That is thinking Black. Wade Nobles, a Black psychiatrist, said that we must overcome conceptual incarceration. That is thinking Black. Thinking Black is applying an Afro-centric or African orientation to reality that is rooted in a history, a reality that is informed by history and is informed by an understanding of the surface as well as the deep structure of African culture. It is of utmost importance that Blacks internalize Afro-centric thought and Malcolm must be credited for providing Blacks in America with the political and spiritual ammunition to enable them to develop a Black consciousness that would prepare, prime and provide them with a foundation for fighting for their liberation with a dignified righteousness!

This was one of Malcolm's greatest contributions to the movement and it did not go unnoticed. His ability to empower Blacks was part of the reason he was considered so dangerous. There were other reasons of course, such as the White power patriarchy's fear and hatred of Black male leadership. But this particular Black consciousness re-awakening was a recognizable potential explosive! It has been over 20 years since I experienced that re-awakening but the memories are still very much alive. Malcolm remains a role model and a major source of inspiration, motivation and confidence, confidence in knowing that I have the correct politics for the spiritual, economic, and social liberation of the

262

oppressed and correct in my determination to struggle against brutality, exploitative methods of our oppressors.

During his lifetime of 40 years, Malcolm received no foundation grants or invitations to any ceremonial awards at the White House, but his memory is cherished more than many other Black leaders in history. He met the emotional needs of Black folks. On a personal level his inspiration and influence has instill in other the foundation of Black Thought and the need for continuous Black struggle.

So enamored was I by Malcolm that one of the greatest tributes/compliments paid me occurred after I had given a lecture at a college and a woman came over to me and said how much she enjoyed my talk especially the question and answer period. Then she said, "You know, you sounded just like a female Malcolm X." That made my day. On another occasion, a student told me during a faculty confab, "You know Gloria, you and Malcolm are the only two people I know that can insult a person and make it sound like you're giving them an important lesson. You say it with a smile and with humor, but if anyone else said the same thing it would be considered an insult." In the late '60's I did not speak of Malcolm in terms of African epistemology, I was too busy preaching his words and fighting for the cause! But over the years, I have come to realize the extent to which Malcolm's conceptual messages have been suppressed by the politics of the Eurocentric masculine knowledge-validation process, i.e. Black knowledge being validated by Eurocentric masculine thought and criteria, which is based on white experiences. Malcolm's Afro-centric style, behavior, thought process, was in a sense unfathomable to the white male dominated media. In most instances, they were incapable of understanding or comprehending Malcolm. In other instances, their resentment and rejection of him dictated their behavior. Additionally, their ingrained fear and hatred of Black male leadership that could not be manipulated, contributed to their attempts to de-evaluate and discredit him. However, it is important to recognize and discuss those specific Afro-centric qualities.

The majority of European writers insist upon using Euro-centric masculinist knowledge claims for validation of Malcolm and construct behavioral theories based on white cultural values. Sociology professor, Chandra Talapade Mohanty in her outstanding paper on "Alternative Epistemology" speaks of four criteria used by African-Americans in evaluating knowledge - claims from a Black point of view. These characteristics are: 1) the use of dialogue in assessing knowledge claims; 2) the centrality of personal expressiveness; 3) the ethic of personal accountability; and 4) concrete experience as a criterion of meaning. I shall discuss how Malcolm epitomized these characteristics and hence part of the reason for his popularity among Blacks.

First, the use of dialogue in assessing how we as Blacks, know what we know: Contemporary African-Americans communities place a high value on the spoken word. There is a call and response discourse mode among African-Americans, composed of spontaneous verbal and nonverbal interactions between speaker and listener. Geneva Smitherman points out … "We are talking ... about an interactive network in which the fundamental requirement is the active participation of all individuals. This is best illustrated in traditional Black church services. Malcolm and his audiences exemplified this discourse. The claps, a-men comers, laughter, and shouts of encouragement and expressions of pleasure, all validate the spoken word. Smitherman continues. ..."for ideas to be tested and validated, all parties must engage in the process. To sit there, disagree, and say nothing is considered "cheating." Connection rather than separation is an essential component in the process of validation of Black leaders and followers.

The second characteristic, the centrality of personal expressiveness: Black culture allows its members considerably greater freedom to assert and express themselves than does White culture. Black culture values individual regulated self-assertion. It also values spontaneous expression of feeling. A major component of personal expressiveness is the appropriateness of emotion in dialogues. Rather than judging an emotional speaker as being irrational or out of control, the use of emotions and feelings is seen

264

as an indication of sincerity. When you see the white press showing pictures of Blacks with mouth wide open, supposedly ranting and raving, they present this as an indication of irrationality. This is a case of their trying to validate our behavior by their rules. Another component of personal expressiveness is in the expectation of personal style or individual uniqueness. Black speakers frequently use rhythms and vocal inflections to convey meanings. The sound of what is being said is just as important *as* the sense of the words. Both sound and sense are used to deliver the word. The effect achieved is the conveyance of a psycho cognitive message. It is nearly impossible to filter out the strictly linguistic-cognitive abstract meaning through the socio-cultural psycho-emotive meanings. In one of his speeches, the subject of violence came up and Malcolm said to his audience, "So I don't believe in violence, uh, that's why I want to stop it." To fully appreciate this comment you would have to *hear* it. It is loaded with the sound and sense of the words.

The third characteristic, the ethic of personal accountability: Not only must individuals work out their own knowledge-claims though dialogue, and present those claims in a style proving their concern for their ideas, individuals are expected to assume personal accountability for the knowledge-claims they propose. Or, "practice what you preach." Blacks disagree with the white belief that probing into an individual's personal viewpoint is outside the boundaries of discussion. This is because they feel that all views expressed and actions taken derive from a central set of core beliefs that cannot be other than personal. From this perspective, knowledge-claims made by individuals respected for their moral and ethical values carry more weight than those offered by less respected figures Elijah Muhammad spoke one brand of morality and practiced another, and this was unacceptable to Malcolm.

The final feature of this Afro-centric epistemology *is* the importance placed on concrete lived experience in assessing knowledge-claims. Those individuals who have lived the things they claim to be "experts" about are more believable and have more credibility than those who have merely experienced them through books or reason that such things must exist, Blacks are quick to ridicule "educated fools" who have knowledge but not wisdom. So Malcolm was very believable to all of us who have: struggled through racist education systems, income below the poverty level; jived in urban ghettos; been in jail; gained religion; hustled; pimped; and been self-educated.

The charisma, charm, and deep attraction that Malcolm possessed had its roots in African epistemology and African culture. Those Black audiences who did not deny their Black culture, and were able to get past the Eurocentric masculinist imposed mode of thinking easily and readily understood his messages.

Originally Composed & Published 5.19.87